JOIN MY READERS' GROUP FOR UPDATES AND FUTURE RELEASES

Please join my Readers' Group so i can send you a free book, as well as updates and information about future releases, etc.

See the back of the book for details on how to sign up.

The Called Series Collection - Volume 2

Isaiah, Deborah, and Enoch

Published by:

Kenneth A. Winter

WildernessLessons, LLC

Richmond, Virginia

United States of America

kenwinter.org

wildernesslessons.com

Edited by Sheryl Martin Hash

Cover design by Scott Campbell Design

ISBN 978-1-9568663-0-8 (soft cover)

ISBN 978-1-9568663-1-5 (e-book)

ISBN 978-1-9568663-2-2 (large print)

Library of Congress Control Numbers:

A Prophet Called Isaiah 2021925004

A Judge Called Deborah 2022904324

A Friend Called Enoch 2022914670

References to *The Book of Enoch* are taken from *The Book of Enoch,* The Apocrypha and Pseudepigrapha of the Old Testament, edited by H. R. Charles Oxford, published by The Clarendon Press

CONTENTS

A PROPHET CALLED ISAIAH

A JUDGE CALLED DEBORAH

A FRIEND CALLED ENOCH

A PROPHET
CALLED ISAIAH
KENNETH A. WINTER

DEDICATION

Now these are the gifts Christ gave to the church: the apostles, the prophets, the evangelists, and the pastors and teachers.
Ephesians 4:11

~

In memory of Keith Thomas,
and in honor of the many others whom God has also used over the years to speak truth into my life.

~

PREFACE

This fictional novella is part of a series titled, *The Called,* which is about ordinary people God called to use in extraordinary ways. We often tend to elevate the people we read about in Scripture and place them on a pedestal far beyond our reach. We think, "Of course God used them. They had extraordinary strength or extraordinary faith. But God could never use an ordinary person like me."

That is a lie the evil one would love for us to believe. He would love for us to think we can't possibly be used by God because we are too ordinary. But the reality is that throughout history God has used the ordinary to accomplish the extraordinary – and He has empowered them through His Holy Spirit.

This story is about the life of one of those ordinary people – Isaiah, the prophet. Like many of you, throughout much of my life, i have been greatly encouraged by the promises contained in the book of Isaiah. Most notably, the Lord chose Isaiah to announce many of the promises related to the coming Messiah. We remember many of those prophecies each year at Christmastime as we recall how they were fulfilled through the advent of Jesus.

But the promises do not stop with the first coming of Jesus. The promises continue to point to the realities that will be fulfilled in the second coming of Jesus – when He returns to establish His kingdom on earth from the throne He will establish in the new Jerusalem. All things will be made new, and as George Frideric Handel wrote using some of Isaiah's words in his great work, "Messiah, an Oratorio," our returning Lord will reign forever and ever. Oh, what a day that will be!

My familiarity with those promises from the book Isaiah was my motivation for writing this story about the person of Isaiah. The foundation for this novella comes from the books of 2 Kings, chapters 12 through 21; 2 Chronicles, chapters 24 through 33, as well as Isaiah itself. As I began to study those passages more closely, i became increasingly aware of the family relationship Isaiah had with the kings of Judah, specifically kings Uzziah, Jotham, Ahaz, Hezekiah, and Manasseh. These were the kings to whom God was directing Isaiah to deliver what, in many instances, were very difficult messages.

The family relationships bring to light an internal conflict Isaiah may have felt when God compelled him to convey those messages. Also, because Isaiah had been close to the kings growing up, he had a unique platform from which to write about the One who will one day sit on the throne of Judah – the One who is King of kings and Lord of lords. But don't lose sight of the fact that Isaiah was a flawed, ordinary man placed in God-ordered circumstances to be a follower through whom God would accomplish extraordinary things.

So, i hope you will sit back and enjoy this walk through Isaiah's life. The story, though based on the Scriptures i have already mentioned, has also been shaped by the writings of Josephus, the early historian of the church, and by certain rabbinical teachings recorded in the Talmud. On a number of occasions, i have added fictional elements to help fill in missing details about Isaiah's story. My goal is not to detract from Scripture in any way; rather, I want to help Isaiah's personal story become even more alive in our minds and in our hearts as we read his writings.

Most of the characters in the story come directly from Scripture – you will easily recognize them. However, where the Bible is silent, i have chosen to add background details about the characters that are either fictional or conjectures not confirmed in Scripture. These details are added to further the telling of the story. As i already mentioned, a few of the characters are completely fictional.

Throughout the stories, some instances of dialogue are direct quotes from Scripture. Whenever i am quoting Scripture, you will find that it has been italicized. The Scripture references are included in the back of this book. Those remaining instances of dialogue not italicized are part of the fictional story in order to help advance the storyline. However, i have endeavored to use Scripture as the basis in forming any added dialogue spoken by a historical character with the intent that i do not detract from the overall message of God's Word.

Finally, my prayer is, that as you read this story, you will see Isaiah, his family, and the kings of Judah through new eyes – and be challenged to hear and see the prophecies of God through their eyes. And most importantly, you will be challenged to be an "ordinary" follower with the willingness and faith to be used by God in extraordinary ways … for His glory!

~

1

A PROPHET'S EXAMPLE

My grandfather, King Joash, was the eighth king of our southern kingdom of Judah. Approximately 100 years before his reign, the nation of Israel split into two kingdoms – the northern kingdom, which retained the name Israel, and the southern kingdom taking the name Judah, the tribal name of King David.

I was sitting in the Great Hall of the palace several years ago, dressed in my royal splendor, thinking how privileged I was to be a member of the royal line of David, Solomon, and Joash. Jotham, the coregent (joint ruler) at the time, was addressing routine matters brought before him. I watched him, thinking surely there were other officials in the palace who could preside over such trivial matters.

Suddenly, a servant announced the arrival of a prophet of God named Amos, who said he needed to speak with the coregent at once. I had heard of Amos; he was born here in Judah but moved to Israel after he declared God was sending him there.

. . .

Amos was originally a shepherd from the rural area of Tekoa here in Judah. He had no special training as a prophet, but apparently Jehovah God called him to leave the grazing fields to carry His message to the palace of Israel. It sounded a little questionable to me.

He did not wait for Jotham to direct him forward. Rather, he boldly approached the throne and began speaking, with no regard for the official he had just interrupted.

"Coregent," Amos began, "you must listen to this message from the Lord that Jeroboam II, king of Israel, has rejected. This is what the Lord says: '*O people of Israel and Judah – the entire family I rescued from Egypt – from among all the families on the earth, I chose you alone.*[1]

"'That is why I must punish you for all your sins. When the war trumpet blares, shouldn't the people be alarmed? When disaster comes to a city, isn't it because the Lord planned it? But always, first of all, I warn you through my servants the prophets. I, the Sovereign Lord, have now done this.[2]

"'The lion has roared – tremble in fear! The Sovereign Lord has spoken – I dare not refuse to proclaim His message!'[3]

"And coregent, *this is what the Lord says* specifically *to the people of Judah: 'You have sinned again and again, and I will not forget it. I will not let you go unpunished any longer! You have rejected the laws of the Lord, refusing to obey Me. You have been led astray by the same lies that deceived your ancestors. So I will send fire down upon you, and all the fortresses of Jerusalem will be destroyed.'"*[4]

I watched closely for Jotham's reaction. Would he become angry as the king of Israel had done? Would he have the prophet forcibly removed? What would he say? I didn't need to wait long for his answer.

• • •

"May God be merciful to His servant, Jotham, and to the people He has set apart for Himself! Forgive us of our sins, O God, and turn Your wrath away from us.

"Amos, what can I do to appease God's wrath and lead our people to do what is right in His eyes?"

Jotham's humble and contrite response surprised me. He obviously viewed this prophet as someone who was highly credible. I realized then how great a burden the weight of this counsel was for this prophet of God.

I had witnessed many bring their counsel before the king over the years, including me. But I had rarely seen that counsel borne from such godly wisdom.

As Jotham listened intently to Amos's every word, I knew his desire was to lead the people back to a right relationship with God. I realized that despite our lifelong friendship, I would never have the influence over Jotham that this prophet of God did.

At that moment, I came face to face with a sense of my own inadequacy and my own insignificance. I began to envy this prophet of God. Though he smelled like sheep and dressed in tatters, I realized he was the most important person in the room – even more important than the coregent himself. He was delivering a message from Jehovah God, and there was nothing of greater consequence than that!

~

2

MY EARLY YEARS IN THE PALACE

My father, Amoz, and his much older brother, Amaziah, were the sons of King Joash. My grandfather was assassinated by two of his trusted advisers while my father was still a young lad, so I know him only through the stories I'm told. My uncle Amaziah became the ninth king of Judah.

I never knew my uncle either because he was assassinated twenty-five years before I was born. He had provoked a war with the northern kingdom of Israel. During that war, his army suffered a humiliating defeat that led to portions of Jerusalem being destroyed and the treasury of the temple and the kingdom being pillaged. The people of Judah blamed my uncle for the defeat, and it was several of his officers who murdered him.

His son, Uzziah, became the tenth king of Judah when he was only sixteen years old. He, however, quickly gained favor with the people. The nation prospered under his leadership and again achieved the wealth and prestige it had enjoyed during the reign of my ancestor King Solomon.

• • •

Cousin Uzziah refortified the walls of Jerusalem and strengthened its defenses by placing machines on the wall towers at the gates that would shoot arrows and hurl large stones. He reorganized and reequipped the army into an effective fighting force. He successfully introduced new methods of agriculture and had a multitude of water cisterns dug throughout the land.

Why was King Uzziah so successful? Two reasons. First, he did what was pleasing in God's sight and enjoyed His favor. Second, he did what was pleasing because he sought God and heeded the wise counsel of the prophet Zechariah.

By the time I was born, Uzziah had already reigned for twenty-five years and was widely respected abroad, even to the entrance of Egypt. Growing up as a member of the royal family in his palace, I, too, enjoyed the many privileges a favored king possesses – though I was far removed from the order of royal succession.

Jotham, Uzziah's eldest son – my first cousin once removed – was, in fact, the heir to the throne. He was two years younger than I, so we became fast friends early on. People used to tell us we were inseparable, much like our fathers had been during their childhood.

When I was seven and Jotham was five, his mother gave birth to a little girl, Nebiah. By the time she was old enough to walk, she began to join Jotham and me on our adventures instead of playing at home with her sisters. We tried everything we could to discourage Nebiah, but nothing worked, and soon the three of us were almost constant companions. To tell the truth, as I got older, I actually started to enjoy her company.

Prince Jotham and I shared the same tutors and received the same quality of education. Eventually we became very competitive in just about everything, including our academic studies, our hunting skills, and our athletic pursuits. We often slipped away from the palace and spent our afternoons exploring the hills outside of Jerusalem. I'm not sure which we enjoyed more – escaping the watchful eyes of our chaperones or exploring the countryside.

Jotham, Nebiah, and I were exploring some caves outside the city one day when a messenger arrived with a rather stern note for Jotham. We were to return to the palace immediately! We knew we must be in trouble but couldn't figure out why this adventure was causing more of a stir than our previous ones.

When we got to the palace, Jotham was directed into the Great Hall to see his father while Nebiah and I were told to wait outside. He came out a little while later, looking very somber.

"My father has done something terrible!" Jotham exclaimed. "Apparently, he entered the Lord's sanctuary in the temple this morning and personally burned incense on the altar."

We all knew that was something only priests whom God has set apart for that work should do. Not even the king has been given that privilege by God.

"The high priest, Azariah, together with eighty other priests entered the sanctuary and confronted my father saying, '*It is not for you to burn incense to the Lord. Get out of the sanctuary for you have sinned. The Lord God will not honor you for this!*'[1]

"Father was furious they had spoken to him in such a way, and he refused to set down the incense burner he was holding. But suddenly the ground underneath the temple began to shake!"

~

3

THE COREGENCY OF UZZIAH AND JOTHAM

~

"The shaking of the ground under the temple was so violent the walls and ceiling of the temple began to shift," Jotham continued. "Within moments, a fissure appeared in the exterior masonry wall, and the sun shone brightly across my father's face. The priests turned ashen as they looked in horror at my father.

"His forehead was suddenly covered with leprosy, and it quickly began to spread! The priests rushed him out of the temple, and he secluded himself in the Great Hall. He is planning to move into a nearby house isolated from everyone else. He has designated me to be his coregent over the palace and the government!"

At the age of twenty, Jotham's life had radically changed … and so had mine. He was no longer the carefree, fun-loving, self-indulgent son of a king; he was now my ruler. We had always known this day would come, but we hadn't expected it to occur so soon!

• • •

Up until that moment, my role had always been as Jotham's companion and friend. I was there to encourage him and, on occasion, give him a word of counsel. But now, there were many royal advisers who would step into that role.

Jotham invited me to sit in the Great Hall once he assumed his position on the throne. I had no official role other than that of being his trusted friend. But I did listen with interest as the affairs of the nation were discussed and decided.

One of the outcomes of King Uzziah's reign was the strengthening of what he saw as two critical alliances. One alliance was to strengthen the kingdom from within, and the other was an alliance he made outside the kingdom.

Soon after Jotham was made coregent, his father arranged for him to marry Princess Ahio. She was the daughter of Azrikam, an influential and wealthy leader of the tribe of Benjamin. He was a descendant of our first king, Saul, also of the tribe of Benjamin.

The marriage was arranged to strengthen the unity of the two tribes that together form the southern kingdom of Judah. It was a uniting of the house of Saul with the house of David. Though it had been over 150 years since the other ten tribes of the nation of Israel had divided to form the kingdom of Israel to the north, Uzziah wanted to assure the alliance of the two remaining tribes remained strong.

The alliance he formed outside the kingdom was with the Assyrians. Uzziah knew all too well that his father's downfall was a result of his defeat by the northern kingdom. Though Judah had not been destroyed, the defeat was unmistakable. Uzziah knew if Israel had been allied with the Assyrians, Judah would have been annihilated.

• • •

He fully intended that no such union would ever come to pass. The best way to ensure that was for him to establish a strong coalition with the Assyrians. He received his greatest assistance in establishing that alliance from the northern kingdom of Israel itself. They had subsequently chosen to join forces with the king of the Arameans – the enemy of the Assyrians. The adage, "the enemy of my enemy is my friend" certainly rang true, and King Uzziah and King Tiglath-Pileser III of Assyria entered a mutually advantageous partnership.

Less than a year after their marriage, Ahio and Jotham had a son, Ahaz, the heir to the throne. With Jotham now completely absorbed in his responsibilities as coregent, husband, and father, he and I spent little time together. I soon found myself passing more and more time with Nebiah.

Over time, Nebiah's and my friendship developed into something more. The entire palace started to notice our relationship, including her mother, Queen Jerushah. One day, I received a summons to come before Jotham.

"Isaiah," he said, "I would not normally be the one to have this conversation with you. But as you know, my father is unable to allow anyone to see him, so the responsibility has fallen to me. He and my mother have both been in communication with me regarding the growing interest between you and my sister, Nebiah.

"My father has always seen marriage as a way to form political alliances – as demonstrated by my own marriage. He intends to have my sister marry someone who will further strengthen our political agreement with the Assyrians.

"My mother, on the other hand, is determined that Nebiah marry a man who shares our faith in Jehovah God. My parents have left the final decision up to me!"

~

4

THE KING IS DEAD

I feared Jotham was about to be the bearer of bad news.

"You are my father's cousin and have always been my friend," he said. "My family has considered you a member of our family since we were children. The blood that courses through your veins is of royal heritage. Your love and loyalty for the king, as well as for me as his coregent, are without question.

"You have honored our family, and now we would like to honor you. I have informed my parents of my decision, and they have also granted their permission for you to marry my sister. And as your friend and regent, I am pleased to bring you the news."

I could not contain my joy! "You honor me, my sovereign and friend, with your great favor," I said. "You have brought joy to both Nebiah and me, and we thank you for this great kindness!"

• • •

Our union would accomplish two things for me. It would further solidify my position within the royal court of Judah. And most importantly, I would be marrying the woman I loved, who was also my best friend.

Six months later, our royal wedding took place at the palace. It was a joyful day filled with heartfelt wishes and blessings. Even King Uzziah attended – albeit from a distance. Screening was set up in one corner of the hall so he would not be visible to guests, but he could still hear all the festivities. Nebiah and I felt greatly blessed by Jehovah God as we retired for the evening.

Our bliss was shattered early the next morning, though, when one of the servants interrupted our sleep with the message: "King Uzziah is dead!"

Shock settled in as the family grappled with the news. We all knew the king's leprosy was getting worse, but none of us expected this. He was my king, my cousin – and now my father-in-law. I especially felt sorry for Jotham. He wasn't really given the opportunity to grieve his father's passing. Instead, he was immediately thrust into the singular role as king.

Though he had served as coregent, he had done so in the shadow of his father. Now that shadow was gone. The coregency had still been a part of his father's reign. Now Jotham would be weighed and assessed on his own merits.

Nebiah and I did our best to console one another, and together we attempted to console Queen Jerushah. But we all knew we needed to help the people of our kingdom mourn the passing of their king. We would need to grieve later. For now, we needed to remain strong.

• • •

A few nights after the king's death, I was experiencing a fitful night's sleep. All at once, I seemed to be in a crowd of people gathered in a magnificent temple. The building was far grander than anything I had ever seen, including the temple here in Jerusalem.

It was also much larger. I could not see the walls opposite where I was standing. They were too far away for me to make them out. I turned to ask the people standing beside me where I was. But they were bowed on bent knees with arms uplifted.

At first I thought I was at a memorial gathering for King Uzziah. But then I began to hear what the crowd was saying. With one voice they were calling out, *"Holy, holy, holy is the Lord of Heaven's Armies! The whole earth is filled with His glory!"*(1)

I followed their gaze and could make out the shape of a throne in the distance. It was elevated high off the ground in what I presumed was the middle of the temple. Then I realized someone was seated on the throne.

As I watched, a host of what I now believe were angels encircled the throne. They were mighty men – larger than any I have ever seen. I've heard stories about the Philistine Goliath, but these men were even bigger than how he was described. And each of these men had six wings!

I was mesmerized as I watched them. With two of their wings, the angels were covering their faces. With two, they covered their feet, and with the remaining two they were flying around the throne.

They, too, were calling out, *"Holy, holy, holy is the Lord of Heaven's Armies! The whole earth is filled with His glory!"*(2)

. . .

However, the sound of their voices shook the temple to its very foundation. And soon the entire building began to fill with what looked like smoke.

It was then I realized who was seated on the throne. Somehow, I had entered the presence of Jehovah God, and it was the train of His robe filling the temple. I fell to my knees and cried out in fear.

~

5

"HERE I AM. SEND ME."

"*It's all over!"* I cried out. *"I am doomed, for I am a sinful man. I have filthy lips, and I live among a people with filthy lips. Yet, I have seen the King, the Lord of Heaven's Armies."*(1)

I could no longer look at the One on the throne. My body was weighed down by my sin. But soon I felt something hovering over me. With all my strength, I forced myself to look up. Flying above me was one of the angelic beings. He was holding a burning coal with a pair of tongs.

I suspected the coal had been taken from the burning altar that stood before the throne. He reached toward me with the coal. I tried to back away, but I could not move. He touched my lips with the coal, and as he did, he said: *"See, this coal has touched your lips. Now your guilt is removed, and your sins are forgiven."*(2)

. . .

The weight I had felt was instantly gone. I looked at the One seated on the throne and heard Him say, *"Whom should I send as a messenger to this people? Who will go for Us?"*[3]

Immediately I rose to my feet and cried out, *"Here I am. Send me!"*[4]

My words echoed in my ears. Had I said them out loud? I must have ... because every eye in the room had now turned toward me – even the eyes of the Lord! *"Yes, go!"* the Lord said. *"But tell My people this: 'You will hear My words, but You will not understand. You will see what I do, but you will not perceive its meaning.'"*[5]

"Lord, how long must I do this?" I asked.[6]

"Until their cities are destroyed, with no one left in them," He answered. *"Until their houses are deserted and the whole country is an utter wasteland. Until I have sent everyone away to distant lands, and the entire land of Israel lies deserted. Even if only a remnant survives, like a tree that is cut down, the stump will be a holy seed that will grow again."*[7]

I knew I could not speak the words I was thinking. My heart was broken by God's promise of destruction. I wanted to shout, "No, Lord! Do not destroy our cities, our houses, and our nation!" I did not want to be the bearer of that news!

I looked at Him, and His eyes penetrated my soul. I began to panic. I wanted to flee from what He was telling me to do. But I knew I could not.

As much as I hated to hear those words, I knew God's punishment was just because of our sinful actions. And now, that same God was commanding me to deliver His message.

• • •

At that moment, I felt as if I were being swallowed by a giant whirlwind. I fell backward into a bottomless funnel. I grabbed wildly, trying to find something to hold on to, but to no avail. The whirlwind unexpectedly stopped, just as a familiar voice called out to me.

"Isaiah, what has come over you?" Nebiah asked. "Wake up, Isaiah!"

Gradually, I opened my eyes but was completely disoriented. I was covered in perspiration, and my heart was racing. I realized I was waking up from a dream. But was it a dream? It seemed so real!

I raised my fingers to feel the spot where the hot coal had touched my lips. I could still feel the sensation. It may have occurred in a dream, but I knew it was very real!

Nebiah's eyes were full of worry. "What is it, Isaiah?" she asked. "What's wrong? Were you having a dream?"

I paused for a moment to collect my thoughts. I sensed the Spirit of God helping me understand what had just taken place.

"Jehovah God has come to me in a dream!" I said. "Though I was asleep, the dream was real. He has chosen me to be His prophet. He has chosen me to tell His people what He is going to do!

"He has placed me in the palace – not to be a king – but to be a prophet to the kings. He has placed me among His people to be a prophet to His people. And I believe He has placed me among His people to tell them about a King who will reign over all kings when He comes one day!

. . .

"Nebiah, He has shown me I have been a man of unclean lips. But He has cleansed my lips and made them into an instrument He can use. He has shown me He already gave me visions even while your father was still alive. But I didn't have ears to hear or eyes to see them at the time. Neither did I have a cleansed mouth with which to repeat them. But now, all that has changed!"

6

COMPLETELY DEPENDENT UPON GOD

~

"The day is dawning," I declared, "and the time has come for me to stand before Jotham and our people and proclaim the Word of the Lord. Pray for me, Nebiah, that I will have the strength and the courage to say all that Jehovah God has told me to say."

I thought back to the day the prophet Amos delivered the Lord's message of judgment to Jotham. Little had I known then the impact that conversation would have on me now as I sought to walk in obedience to God.

Jotham had asked, "Amos, what can I do to appease God's wrath and lead our people to do what is right in His eyes?"

Amos had counseled Jotham to seek the Lord God Jehovah in all things. He was relentless in his opinion that our relationship with God, as His chosen people, was a moral contract. If we fail to honor the requirements of God's law, we cease to be in relationship with Him.

• • •

Amos also taught that our dependence on God is a requirement toward finding fulfillment in Him – personally and as a nation. He repeatedly told Jotham that apart from God, he would accomplish nothing.

He continued by reminding Jotham that our worship is not expressed to God through ceremonial actions; rather, it is demonstrated through genuine righteousness in our acts of service and justice.

Amos stood before Jotham and proclaimed, "The Lord showed me this vision. *I saw the Lord standing beside a wall that had been built using a plumb line. He was checking it with a plumb line to see if it was straight. And the Lord said to me, 'Amos, what do you see?'"*

"I answered, 'A plumb line.' And the Lord replied, 'I will test My people with this plumb line. I will no longer ignore all their sins.'"[1]

Amos may not have received his education in the school of the prophets, but every counselor and witness present in the hall – as well as the coregent himself – took note of this message. And I had been no exception. Even that day I sensed Jehovah God had positioned me in the Great Hall not for the wisdom I might speak, but so I might learn from what I heard and adjust my life to that same plumb line.

There was no question how God had used His prophet Amos to change the heart of Jotham. Since then, he had done much that was good and pleasing in the sight of the Lord. But, like his father, he had not destroyed the pagan shrines where many of our people continued to offer sacrifices and burn incense to false gods. And Amos had never failed to remind him of the plumb line.

I knew God had given Amos his message through a series of visions, similar to what I had just experienced. The king of Israel had rejected the message, but Jotham had not. Would my words as a prophet be rejected or received? I decided it was time for me to seek out Amos.

When I arrived at his lodgings, he did not seem surprised to see me. Neither was he surprised to hear the account of my vision of the Lord.

"God chooses His servants," Amos said, "not based on their abilities but based on their availability. He called me from the pasture and you from the palace. But neither of us has received training from men. In that way, we are completely dependent upon God.

"As a prophet, your responsibility is saying everything God tells you to say. You cannot leave anything out or add anything to it. You will be responsible for communicating God's message – but you will not be responsible for how it is received.

"My greatest grief is seeing God's people rejecting God's Word. He does not permit me to rest until I have spoken the message He has given me. The burden is great, and the only thing that can ease it is delivering the words of the Lord.

"The Lord has also shown me, and I believe He has told me to tell you, 'Write down the words I give you. These words are not only for this current generation but also for the generations to come. Record my words so they can be passed from one generation to the next.'

"Further the Lord has said, '*One day I will restore the fallen house of David. I will repair its damaged walls. From the ruins I will rebuild it and restore its former glory. And Israel will possess what is left of Edom and all the nations I have called to be Mine.*'[2]

. . .

"The Lord has spoken, and He will do these things. The time will come! Be faithful, Isaiah. Do not shy away from what God has told you to do and say – for He will bring it all to pass at the right time."

"May God find me faithful in all He has told me to do and say," I responded as I prepared to return to the palace.

It was now time to tell my king the commission I had received from Jehovah God.

~

7

A KING REPENTS FOR HIS PEOPLE

~

The next morning, Jotham called to me as I entered the Great Hall. "Where were you yesterday, Isaiah?"

"I spent the day with the prophet Amos," I replied.

"What could you possibly have wanted to speak with him about?" he asked jokingly.

"I was in need of his counsel," I responded. "Something has happened I must tell you about. But I must speak to you not only as my king but also as my friend."

Jotham could see I was serious, so he immediately sent away the officials standing before him, and he motioned for me to take their place.

. . .

"I hear the urgency in your voice, Isaiah," Jotham said empathetically. "I will listen to you as your friend and attempt to hear your words with the wisdom of a king. Tell me what has happened."

"The night before last," I began, "the Lord came to me in a dream – or rather, I entered into His presence while I was sleeping."

I then began to relay the events of my dream as clearly as I could recall them, not leaving out a single detail. Jotham never interrupted me but listened intently throughout my account. His expression became even more serious as I told him what God had said about the destruction of our cities, our houses, and our nation.

Then I told him, "I know I am not worthy to be the prophet of God on my own merits. But I also know He has placed this mantle upon me, and I can do no less. Hear the words I have told you, my friend – and my king – for thus has the Lord said."

Jotham did not speak at first. Rather, he stood to his feet and ripped his robe before falling to his knees. Then he cried out, "Forgive us, Oh God, for our transgressions against You! Forgive us – not because we deserve it – but because You are a merciful God. Forgive us for being a stiff-necked people who have rebelled against you from one generation to the next. Forgive us, and cleanse us of our wicked ways!

"Forgive me as the king of this people. In your sovereignty, You have placed me in authority over them. They will not turn to You with all their hearts if I do not do so. Lead me in the way that You would have me go that I might live in obedience to You!"

Jotham continued to cry out to God in repentance for the remainder of the morning. At first, those standing in the hall did not know what to do. But as Jotham continued to call out to God, they began to fall to their knees, one by one, crying out to God.

By the time Jotham was done, everyone in the hall was on their knees and the sound of weeping echoed throughout the palace. Jotham turned his attention back to me and asked, "Oh man of God, what would Jehovah God have me do?"

"King Jotham," I replied, "He would have you seek Him and follow Him with all your heart, soul, mind, and strength. He would have you lead His people to obey His laws and all His precepts. You are to rebuild that which has been broken and cast out anyone who continues to rebel against Him. Thus has the Lord said!"

It was obvious Jotham intended to do just that. He had witnessed the downfall of his father due to his pride and had heard about the failures of his grandfather due to his disobedience. Jotham vowed to not repeat those failures but to follow the Lord completely.

He told me I was to stand before him each day in the Great Hall – no longer solely as a trustworthy friend – but now as the prophet of the Almighty God, ensuring Jehovah was honored through the king's every word and every action. From that day forward no one held a higher position of counsel to Jotham than I did.

The king knew the enemies of God and His people were a threat to the kingdom of Judah. The kings of the Ammonites, Aramites, and the northern kingdom of Israel continued to threaten further attack upon Jerusalem. Jotham knew the kingdom's defenses must be strengthened.

He completed the work begun by his father to rebuild the city gates and the defensive wall that overlooked the Kidron Valley. He assigned additional men and resources to the task so the work could be completed more quickly. But he knew that alone would not be enough.

8

BUT HE DID NOT DESTROY THE PAGAN SHRINES

Over the next few years, Jotham led his people to establish new towns in the hill country of Judah so Jerusalem would no longer be isolated. He also led them to construct fortresses and watchtowers in the wooded areas surrounding the city. God granted him a reprieve from any enemy attacks while the defenses were being made ready.

But four years after King Uzziah died, Shanip (the king of Ammon) led his army to attack Jerusalem. Our people have a long history with the Ammonites. They are the descendants of Lot, the nephew of our patriarch Abraham. Long before the days of the exodus, Abraham permitted Lot to choose which land he and his offspring would inhabit. Lot chose the land on the east side of the Jordan River.

Almost 500 years had passed when God led our people to inhabit the Promised Land. He honored the agreement between Abraham and Lot, and instructed Moses: *"Do not bother the Ammonites, nor start a war with them. I have given the land of Ammon to them as their property, and I will not give you any of their land."*[1]

. . .

But over 400 years later, King Nahash of Ammon broke the agreement and threatened to attack some of the cities of Israel and enslave our people. King Saul led our people to defeat the Ammonites so devastatingly that it is written, *"Their army was so badly scattered that no two of them were left together."*(2) It was that victory that united our people from twelve individual tribes into the nation of Israel with Saul as our king.

Forty years after that, King Nahash's son, King Hanun, dishonored King David by disgracing his ambassadors and then foolishly sending their army to conquer Israel. But that army quickly retreated in defeat. Relations with the Ammonites remained quiet for 150 years until the reign of my ancestor King Jehoshaphat, at which time they formed an alliance with the Moabites to again threaten our people.

Those threats and a smattering of scattered skirmishes continued for the 100 years leading up to King Shanip's attack on Jerusalem. But because of Jotham's obedience, Jehovah God enabled Judah to regain its military strength, and the Ammonites were resoundingly defeated. Jotham was careful to give all the glory and honor to Jehovah God.

The Lord instructed me to tell Jotham to extract "an annual tribute of over 3 tons of silver, 50,000 bushels of wheat, and the same quantity of barley" from King Shanip for three years, which he did. The people took notice of Jehovah God's favor upon Jotham, and our surrounding neighbors also paid close heed to his growing power.

Judah prospered while the northern kingdom of Israel looked on with envy. The alliance between Pekah, the king of Israel, and Rezin, the king of the Arameans, continued and they made frequent threats against Jerusalem. But no such attacks occurred during the remainder of Jotham's reign.

. . .

Five years after Jotham became king, God blessed Nebiah and me with our firstborn son. God told me to name him Shear-jashub, which means "a remnant will return." He was to be a constant reminder to me of God's everlasting faithfulness to His people.

As Jotham's son, Ahaz, matured, the king would often have his son by his side so he could observe what it would be like to rule someday. I knew from when we were boys that Jotham had always regretted his father's decision not to include him in affairs of the kingdom. As a result, Jotham had been thrust into his position as coregent with very little preparation. He intended for his son to be better prepared.

But as I watched Ahaz, my spirit was troubled. Though he was still a boy, I did not see an earnestness in Ahaz to seek after God and honor Him. He seemed to be more taken by the luxuries of being king than he was with the solemn duty before God. I expressed my concerns to Jotham, but he dismissed them saying, "It is merely because my son is still a youth."

I feared that was not the case. I also reminded Jotham that he had not yet destroyed the pagan shrines where the people were still offering sacrifices and incense to their false gods. He assured me he was trying to lead the people to destroy the shrines on their own.

But I told him that left to their own devices the people would never choose to do so. I reminded him that his responsibility as their king was to lead them to honor God in ALL they did. Though Jotham aspired to obey God in all things, he failed to do so in this one way. He believed his personal example would be enough – but it was not. And I reminded him there are always consequences for sin.

One night, the Lord placed a song in my heart. My spirit was troubled, but I knew I must sing it to Jotham.

~

9

CLOUDS HOVER OVER THE VINEYARD

~

I entered the Great Hall the next morning singing this song:

"My Beloved had a vineyard on a rich and fertile hill. He plowed the land, cleared its stones, and planted it with the best vines. In the middle He built a watchtower and carved a winepress in the nearby rocks. Then He waited for a harvest of sweet grapes, but the grapes that grew were bitter.

"Now, you people of Jerusalem and Judah, you judge between Me and My vineyard. What more could I have done for My vineyard that I have not already done? When I expected sweet grapes, why did My vineyard give Me bitter grapes?

"Now let Me tell you what I will do to My vineyard: I will tear down its hedges and let it be destroyed. I will break down its walls and let the animals trample it. I will make it a wild place where the vines are not pruned and the ground is not hoed, a place overgrown with briers and thorns. I will command the clouds to drop no rain on it."(1)

. . .

After I finished singing, I said, "Jotham, this is the story of the Lord's people. They are His vineyard. Israel and Judah are His pleasant garden. But there is judgment to come, and lest they repent and turn to Him, He will permit His people to be taken away into captivity. *Clouds hover over Israel and Judah, and one day soon they will blot out the light!"*[2]

Jotham became distraught. "Isaiah, are you telling me there is nothing I can do to stop it? Are you telling me that destruction and captivity will occur despite all I have done? I fear that our destruction will come from within the kingdom even more than it will come from outside the kingdom!"

There were already signs that forces were at work to remove Jotham from the throne. Several advisors who had served his father were expressing concern about the growing alliance between the northern kingdom and the Arameans. They had encouraged Uzziah to enter an alliance with the Assyrians, but now they were suggesting Jotham pay tribute to the Assyrian king and give him control over the defenses of our kingdom.

Few in the palace were concerned about hearing from God or following His direction; most were ready to follow the might of the Assyrians. My voice of reason was carrying less weight in the Great Hall. Yes, I feared destruction and captivity would come all too soon.

I also began to observe those same counselors who were attempting to lead Jotham closer to the Assyrians had now gained the ear of Ahaz. Each day I saw the twenty-year-old heir to the throne being drawn more and more to them and away from his father.

One afternoon Nebiah told me she feared for her brother's safety. She had heard rumors that a pro-Assyrian faction now felt so emboldened they were making plans to force Jotham off the throne. No matter how much she or I tried to warn him, he disregarded our concerns.

A week later, I arrived early one morning at the Great Hall. I hoped to speak with Jotham before the others arrived. I saw him kneeling beside the throne – which was not an unusual sight. I hesitated to interrupt his prayer time, but I knew it was urgent that we speak.

I stood at a respectful distance from the throne and said, "Your majesty, please forgive my intrusion, but I have come to speak with you about a matter of urgency."

I waited a few minutes for him to respond. I presumed he was concluding his prayer time before he answered me. But after considerable time had passed, he still did not acknowledge me.

I walked closer and knelt beside him as if to join him in prayer. When I placed my hand on his shoulder, his body fell forward onto the floor. It was then I saw the hilt of a knife protruding from his chest and his blood-soaked clothing.

His eyes and mouth were open, but he wasn't making a sound. He was no longer breathing. My king, and my friend, was dead!

I called out for help. Within moments, the guards stationed at the outer doors came running. Over the next several hours, I felt like I was falling in the whirlwind from my dream. But this time, it was no dream. King Jotham had been murdered – and everything seemed out of control!

Soon, Queen Ahio and Ahaz arrived. Ahaz was no longer the prince; he was now the king. I watched as he consoled his mother in her grief, but I saw little, if any, sorrow in my nephew. No one seemed to know who had committed this act of treachery. But I feared Ahaz knew only too well.

Funeral arrangements were made. Our new king ascended to the throne. Life in the palace changed. Life in Judah soon changed. The grapes in the vineyard of Judah had just become more bitter!

10

MAHER-SHALAL-HASH-BAZ

The days of mourning for King Jotham had not yet been completed when we learned an army from the north was approaching to lay siege to Jerusalem. King Rezin of Aram and King Pekah of the northern kingdom had apparently determined that Judah would be most vulnerable at this moment.

The army was only two days away from reaching our city. Those of us who gave counsel to the king were divided on what we should do. Those who had advised Jotham to call on Assyrian King Tiglath-Pileser III for protection were now urging Ahaz to quickly do the same. I felt I needed to remind Ahaz their protection would come at a price.

I knew he would be surveying the defenses of the city's water supply to make certain it was adequately secured before the attack. I decided to meet him there so we could talk without the interference of competing voices. I brought my son with me at the Lord's prompting. Ahaz had always been fond of his younger cousin.

. . .

"Your majesty," I began, "the Assyrians would be only too happy to make Judah a part of their growing empire and you a puppet king under the rule of a man who does not fear Jehovah God. Rather, we must turn to the Lord and trust Him to defend us against Israel and Aram.

"Jehovah God has said, *'You do not need to fear the fierce anger of those two burned-out embers, King Rezin and King Pekah.* Yes, they are threatening to invade and install another to replace you as king. But this is what I say: *This invasion will never happen!'"*(1)

Ahaz looked at me in silence as he pondered his decision. "We will do as the Lord has said," he finally replied. "Our fighting men will defend our city and trust Him for the victory – because there is not enough time for me to do anything different."

Amazingly, despite Ahaz's obvious lack of faith, God granted us the victory, and our city withstood the attack. Our enemies retreated to their lands until what I expected would be another day. But instead of rejoicing in the victory God had given us, Ahaz continued to turn away from Him.

Not long after that day, the Lord sent me back to Ahaz with this message: *"Ask Me for a sign to prove that I will crush your enemies as I have promised. Ask for anything you like and make it as difficult as you want."*(2)

But Ahaz refused, saying: *"No, I wouldn't test the Lord like that.*(3)

"All right, then," I replied, "the Lord Himself has chosen the sign. *Look! The virgin will conceive a Child! She will give birth to a son and will call Him Immanuel, meaning 'God is with us.'*(4)

"But before this child is born, *the Lord will bring a terrible curse on you, your nation and your family. You will soon experience greater terror than has been known in all the years since Solomon's empire was divided. The Lord will take the 'razor' – the Assyrians you seek to protect you – and use it to shave off everything: your land, your crops, and your people.*[(5)]

"When they finally stop plundering, few people will be left. The entire land will be one vast brier patch, covered by briers and thorns."[(6)]

I prayed those words would bring Ahaz to repentance, but instead his heart was hardened. He did not receive the word of the Lord. Rather, he did what was right in his own eyes and abandoned all his father had done. Instead of following his father's example, he followed the example of the kings of Israel.

My heart was uplifted by the Lord's promise of the child who would one day be born! But I was heartbroken over the destruction that would first come to my people, my nation, and my family. Ahaz was part of my family. The offspring of Solomon were a part of my family – and all would come under the judgment that God had just declared through me. I looked into the hardness of Ahaz's eyes, and my heart broke even more.

In the days immediately following, Ahaz discharged all the counselors who had loyally served his father – including me. As a member of the royal family, I continued to live in the palace, but I was no longer a part of the king's trusted circle. But Ahaz's insult would not change the fact I am the prophet of the Most High God, and I will bear His message wherever, whenever, and to whomever He chooses.

A short time later, my wife gave birth to our second son, whom the Lord told me to name Maher-shalal-hash-baz, which means "he has made haste to the plunder." God told me that before my son was old enough to call me "papa," the king of Assyria would invade the northern kingdom and carry away their riches.

. . .

The Lord sent me back to Ahaz to declare His words:

"Do not think like everyone else does. Do not be afraid that some plan conceived behind closed doors will be the end of you. Do not fear anything except the Lord Almighty. He alone is the Holy One. If you fear Him, you need fear nothing else. But if you do not, there will be trouble and anguish and dark despair."[7]

However, Ahaz still did not heed the words of the Lord.

~

11

A SON IS BORN TO A FOOLISH KING

~

The announcement of an upcoming birth brings hope to every home – including a palace. King Ahaz proudly proclaimed that his wife, Queen Abijah, was with child. He spoke with great certainty that the child would be a son. The happy news was a welcome relief from the many challenges our kingdom was facing.

Ahaz seemed grateful that he was being congratulated for something. I will confess it was the first positive word I had been able to speak to him since he became king.

He had wasted no time in bringing the images of Baal, which Jehoiada the priest had destroyed one hundred years earlier, back into our kingdom. He seemed intent on following the examples of the disobedient kings of the northern kingdom instead of following the examples set by his father and grandfather.

• • •

He reintroduced the detestable practices of the pagan nations the Lord had driven out of the land ahead of His people under Joshua's leadership. Ahaz offered sacrifices – both animal and human – and burned incense at the pagan shrines Jotham had failed to destroy.

The destruction God had said would come to pass was now beginning to take place. The king of Edom declared war on Judah to recover the town of Elath in the southern part of our kingdom. Edom prevailed and the town Ahaz's grandfather, Uzziah, had rebuilt was lost.

Edom's victory emboldened the Philistine king to raid the towns of Judah located in the foothills along the Negev. They captured and were now occupying six of those villages. King Rezin and King Pekah clearly saw God had withdrawn His hand of protection from Judah, prompting them to redeploy their armies to attack Jericho.

In a single day, King Pekah's army killed 120,000 of our fighting men. Elkanah, Ahaz's second in command, and Azrikam, the king's palace commander, were both killed in that devastating attack. Also, 200,000 women and children were captured by the armies of Israel and taken into exile to Samaria.

Amazingly, they chose not to advance on Jerusalem. Their goal had apparently been to humiliate Ahaz, not kill him. They knew the former would be more painful than the latter.

Even with all that carnage, Ahaz rejected my pleas for him to repent and turn to Jehovah God. But the pagan armies of Israel apparently feared God more than the king of Judah!

When the armies of Israel returned to Samaria, they were met by a prophet of the Lord named Oded. He told them: "*The Lord, the God of your ancestors, was angry with Judah and let you defeat them. But you have gone too far, and all heaven is disturbed! Listen to me and return these captives you have taken, for they are your own relatives. Watch out, because now the Lord's fierce anger has been turned against you!"*[1]

Having heard Oded, some of the leaders of Israel also turned to the armies and said, "*You must not bring the prisoners here! We cannot afford to add to our sins and guilt – or the Lord's fierce anger will be turned against us even more."*[2]

So, to our surprise, they returned the captives to Jericho. They provided them with clothing, sandals, and food from the looting they had seized. Those who were too weak to walk were placed on the backs of donkeys.

As I entered the Great Hall, I cried out, "King Ahaz, there is no question God has been merciful and gracious to the people – and to you! Surely you must see that! Turn from your wicked ways and turn to Him!"

But again, Ahaz hardened his heart. Instead of turning to God, he turned to the king of Assyria, sending him this message: *"I am your servant and your vassal. Come up and rescue me from the attacking armies of Aram and Israel."*[3]

King Tiglath-pileser agreed to do so – but when he arrived in Jerusalem, he came not as a friend or a helper but as a conqueror. Jerusalem had been given into his hands without any resistance.

Ahaz soon realized his error, but his attempted solution was to barter his way out of his mistake. He collected silver and gold from the Lord's temple, the palace, and the homes of all his officials and presented it to the king of Assyria in hopes he would receive it as a gift. Even King Tiglath-pileser looked at Ahaz with disbelief – how could this king be so foolish and naïve?

• • •

From another room in the palace, I heard a baby's cry. Ahaz's son, Hezekiah, had just entered the world.

12

AN ABOMINATION

King Tiglath-pileser attacked the Aramean capital of Damascus, ostensibly to defend Judah. But truth be told, the king of Assyria had already planned to attack Aram for his own personal gain. Now he was being doubly rewarded to do so! The Assyrian army killed King Rezin and led the defeated Aramean soldiers away as captives.

The Aramean women and children did not share the soldiers' fate. Instead, they remained captives in Damascus serving under the brutality of their Assyrian masters. King Tiglath-pileser chose to temporarily remain in that city. From there, he sent word to Ahaz to come to him, demanding that he bring additional payment.

Ahaz swore his allegiance to the Assyrian king after arriving in Damascus. He began to take great pleasure in the things he saw around the city. Ahaz particularly admired an altar used to worship Baal. He had a model of the altar made, together with plans detailing its design, and sent them to one of his priests in Jerusalem with instructions to have the altar built and ready for him when he returned.

Meanwhile, Ahaz's son was now becoming a young lad. He favored his grandfather, Jotham, in appearance and temperament, much more than he did his father. Hezekiah's mother, Queen Abijah, permitted me to spend more and more time with the boy. Although Ahaz no longer listened to a word I said, God was allowing me to be a mentor to Hezekiah.

The Lord showed me He would rebuild Judah through Hezekiah. I was to teach the boy about the laws and ways of Jehovah God. And the young prince, for his part, demonstrated an insatiable thirst to learn and understand.

Queen Abijah subsequently gave birth to two additional sons – the older was named Manasseh and the younger boy named Tiglath in honor of the Assyrian king. Sadly, neither child lived long enough for me to teach them the ways of God.

When Ahaz returned to Jerusalem, he immediately went to look for the altar he had commissioned to be built. After it passed his inspection, the altar was placed in front of the Lord's temple. He then sent word to have his son, Manasseh, brought to him. Ahaz wrapped his arm around his son and proudly showed him the altar as they walked around it. The lad had never received such attention from his father. He was clearly relishing the moment.

But then the mood abruptly changed. Ahaz tied his son's hands and feet, and placed him on the altar. Witnesses gasped in horror. The priests of Baal began to move about the altar, as if they were in a trance, making groaning sounds that seemed to rise from the very pit of hell.

• • •

My son, Shear-jashub, ran to where I was teaching Hezekiah and told me what Ahaz was doing. I immediately ran as quickly as I could to try and stop him – but I was too late. Ahaz had slit his son's throat moments before I arrived. The priests of Baal were gathering the boy's blood into basins. I had never witnessed such an abomination!

"Ahaz, stop! What have you done?" I cried out. "You have murdered your innocent son! You have profaned Jehovah God! You have desecrated His temple! Does nothing good remain within you?"

I knew I could have been executed for speaking to my king that way, but I did not care. I could not stand by silently and not charge him for his evil actions. But he never reacted. He just stood there over his lifeless son, staring blankly into the distance, while the worshipers of Baal continued to cry out around him.

The consequences for my outburst were swift. Members of the palace guard quickly ushered me away. Soon I was informed my family and I were no longer welcome at the palace. We must find other lodging immediately, and I was no longer permitted in the king's hall. I didn't really care because I did not want my family exposed to such an evil king – nor did I want us living under his roof.

I went to our rooms to tell my wife we must pack our belongings; but first, I pulled my family around me. Nebiah was holding our daughter, Hephzibah, who had been born only a few months earlier. I hugged them tightly, together with my sons, Shear-jashub and Maher-shalal-hash-baz, as I cried out to God to deliver His people from this evil king.

As we were leaving the palace, I received a message from Queen Abijah asking if I would continue to teach Hezekiah. She would find a way for me to do so in secret. I knew this was what the Lord wanted, so I sent word back that I would.

13

A SON IS PROMISED, AND A KING DIES

As the days passed, Ahaz ran out of treasures to present to the Assyrian king as tribute. Instead, he embraced the gods of the Assyrians to gain favor with the ruler. But nothing he did seemed to help.

Ahaz became increasingly desperate. He led the people of Judah to abandon the worship of Jehovah God and turn to the pagan gods. He shut the doors of the Lord's temple so no one could worship there. He took the few remaining utensils of worship from the temple and broke them into pieces.

He then set up altars to the pagan gods in every corner of Jerusalem and throughout Judah. Just when it looked as if he could do no worse, he took his son Tiglath to the Valley of Hinnom, on the western side of the city, and sacrificed him in the fire.

Days became weeks, weeks became months, and months became years. I cried out to God to stop Ahaz's madness, and yet it continued. Hunger and misery spread throughout the land, but instead of turning to God, the people shook their fists at Him and cursed Him.

One bright exception was Hezekiah. As he grew in stature, he grew in knowledge and dedication to the Lord – despite the actions of his father. He listened intently as I told him all the Lord was promising would come to pass.

"The Lord has told me to write down all these things as a testimony of what all He will do. The time of darkness and despair will not go on forever. The people who walk in darkness will see a great light – a light that will shine on all who live in the land where death casts its shadow.[(1)]

"God will break the chains that bind His people and the whip that scourges them, just as He did in the days of Moses. But on that day *a Child will be born to us, a Son will be given. And the government will rest on His shoulders. These will be His royal titles: Wonderful Counselor, Mighty God, Everlasting Father, Prince of Peace.*[(2)]

"His ever expanding, peaceful government will never end. He will rule forever with fairness and justice from the throne of His ancestor David. The passionate commitment of the Lord Almighty will guarantee this!"[(3)]

"Isaiah, when will this come to pass?" Hezekiah asked.

"Destruction is certain before the coming of the Promised One," I replied. *The Lord's fist is poised to strike. He will send desolation upon Israel and Judah from a distant land. The Lord says: 'Assyria is the whip of My anger. Its military power is a club in My hand.*[(4)] *Assyria will enslave My people. It will plunder them, trampling them like dirt beneath its feet. But the king of Assyria will not know that it is I who sent him. He will merely think he is attacking My people as part of his plan to conquer the world.'*[(5)]

• • •

"After the Lord has used the king of Assyria to accomplish His purposes in Jerusalem, He will turn against him and punish him for his arrogance. He will completely destroy Assyria's warriors. Only a few will survive – so few that a child could count them![(6)]

"Then at last those left in Israel and Judah will trust the Lord, the Holy One of Israel. They will no longer depend on the Assyrians, who would destroy them. A remnant of them will return. Though the people of Israel are as numerous as the sand on the seashore, only a few of them will return.[(7)]

"The Lord Almighty says: 'My people in Jerusalem, do not be afraid of the Assyrians when they oppress you just as the Egyptians did long ago. It will not last very long. In a little while My anger against you will end, and then My anger will rise up to destroy them. I will cut them down *as an ax cuts down the forest trees in Lebanon.'*[(8)]

"Out of the stump of David's family – your family, Hezekiah – *will grow a shoot – yes, a new Branch bearing fruit from the old root. In that day the wolf and the lamb will live together, the leopard and the goat will be at peace. Calves and yearlings will be safe from lions, and a little child will lead them all."*[(9)]

"Will this occur in my lifetime?" the young prince asked.

"Only Jehovah God knows when these events will unfold," I answered, "and His Promised One will come. In the meantime, we are to honor Him and follow Him with all our hearts, souls, minds, and strength. When you become king, you must do everything you can to lead the people to do the same."

"I will remember His promise," Hezekiah declared, "and I will seek to honor and follow Him in all I do!"

• • •

God mercifully limited Ahaz's days. When the Lord determined Hezekiah was ready to become king, Ahaz died. No one was ever able to explain what caused his death. But on that day, it felt like a great cloud had been lifted off Judah.

~

14

THE TEMPLE IS RESTORED

~

King Hezekiah wasted no time in undoing the evil practices put in place by his father. He had all the pagan shrines and altars removed and destroyed. He smashed the pillars that had been erected for pagan worship, including the Asherah poles.

He even destroyed the bronze serpent Moses had made because the people had turned it into an object of worship. Within the first month of his reign, he reopened the doors of the temple of the Lord and repaired them. He summoned the priests and Levites to meet with him at the courtyard on the east side of the temple.

Hezekiah proclaimed, "*Listen to me, you Levites! Purify yourselves, and purify the temple of the Lord, the God of your ancestors. Remove all the defiled things from the sanctuary. Our ancestors were unfaithful and did what was evil in the sight of the Lord our God.*[1]

. . .

"They abandoned the Lord and His temple; they turned their backs on Him. That is why the Lord's anger has fallen upon Judah and Jerusalem. He has made us an object of dread, horror, and ridicule, as you can so plainly see.[2]

"But now I will make a covenant with the Lord, the God of Israel, so that His fierce anger will turn away from us. My dear Levites, do not neglect your duties any longer! The Lord has chosen you to stand in His presence, to minister to Him, and to lead the people in worship and make offerings to Him."[3]

The Levites got right to work. They purified themselves and began the work to cleanse the temple. They carefully followed the instructions handed down from the Lord through King Solomon. They removed all the defiled things and had them burned in the Kidron Valley.

It took sixteen days before they were able to report back to Hezekiah: "We have purified the temple, the altar of burnt offering, and the table of Show-bread pointing to the presence of God. We have purified all the utensils, including those taken by King Ahaz. Everything is now cleansed and ready for use."

Early the next morning, Hezekiah instructed the city officials to gather at the temple and bring seven bulls, seven rams, seven lambs, and seven male goats to be given as a sin offering. He commanded the priests, who were descendants of Aaron, to sacrifice the animals on the altar of the Lord.

They killed the animals and sprinkled the blood on the altar to make atonement for the sins of all of Israel. Hezekiah stationed the Levites throughout the temple with trumpets, cymbals, harps, and lyres to lead the people in songs of praise and worship from the psalms of David.

When the dedication of the temple was completed, Hezekiah instructed all the people to bring their sacrifices and offerings to be presented to the

Lord. But there were too few priests to accept all the offerings, so Hezekiah directed the Levites to help them.

Every element of pagan worship, including the high places, was destroyed and the temple of the Lord was restored. The people rejoiced because of what God had accomplished so quickly.

Hezekiah then invited everyone throughout Israel and Judah to come to the temple in Jerusalem to celebrate the Passover. His messengers carried letters that read: "Oh people of Israel, return to the Lord. Do not be like your ancestors and relatives who abandoned the Lord and became an object of ridicule. Come to His temple, which He has set apart as holy forever.

"Worship Him so that His fierce anger will turn away from you. For the Lord your God is gracious and merciful. If you return to Him, He will not continue to turn His face from you."[4]

When the people came together, everyone celebrated joyfully for two weeks. Jerusalem had not seen a celebration like this one since the days of King Solomon. God heard the praises of His people from His holy dwelling in heaven. Hezekiah wholeheartedly did what was pleasing and good in the sight of the Lord … and God rewarded His efforts.

15

THE DAYS OF PROSPERITY UNDER HEZEKIAH'S REIGN

The day Hezekiah became king, he arranged for me and my family to move back into the palace. He told me he wanted me close by his side. His mother had preserved our accommodations during our absence and embraced us warmly upon our return.

Hezekiah also immediately restored my position as chief counselor to the king. Though I knew that role would always be secondary to God's call on my life to be His prophet, I was grateful to again have free access to the king and to be a voice of godly wisdom for him. Hezekiah dismissed all those who had served his father and surrounded himself with men who earnestly sought to honor the Lord God Jehovah.

After the celebration at the temple, the king organized the priests and Levites into divisions to present the offerings of the people and lead them in giving thanksgiving and praise to the Lord. The king made a personal contribution from his royal flocks and herds for the daily burnt offerings, as well as for the weekly Sabbath festival.

. . .

In turn, he required the people to bring a portion of their income, as prescribed by the Mosaic laws, to the priests and Levites so they could devote themselves fully to the law of the Lord. The people responded with overwhelming generosity, so Hezekiah directed that storerooms be built in the temple to safeguard their gifts.

The people's offerings and the distribution to the priests and Levites were done in a way that honored God. And He, in turn, rewarded Hezekiah and the people for their faithfulness.

The year after Ahaz died, the Lord gave me this message for the Philistines: *"Do not rejoice, you Philistines, that the king who attacked you is dead. For even though that whip is broken, his son will be worse than his father ever was. I will wipe you out with famine.*

"I will destroy the few who remain. A powerful army is coming against you from the north.[1] And it is the Lord who comes before them."

Hearing this word from the Lord, Hezekiah dispatched his army to attack the Philistines starting in the foothills along the Negev. The army of Judah quickly recaptured the six villages seized by the Philistines during Ahaz's reign. Our army then proceeded into Gaza and conquered the remainder of their territory – from their smallest outpost to their largest walled city. The Lord had truly gone before them.

In the fourth year of Hezekiah's reign, the king of Assyria attacked the kingdom of Israel to the north and began a siege on the city of Samaria – just as the Lord had shown me would happen. Despite everything the kings of Israel had seen God do on Hezekiah's behalf, they continued to dishonor God and violate His covenant. The siege lasted for three years until Samaria fell. The Assyrian king deported all the Israelites and scattered them in colonies to multiple cities within Assyria. Through it all, Judah remained unthreatened and unharmed.

• • •

As a matter of fact, throughout the first thirteen years of his reign, Hezekiah experienced great blessings from the Lord. The region of Judah expanded, the people were prosperous, the king's treasury and the temple storehouse continued to grow in bounty and riches. It appeared that God's wrath had been turned away from Judah – at least during the reign of this king.

I couldn't have been prouder of my king and his dedication to the Lord if he were my own son. In many respects, I loved him like one of my own sons. Never once did he turn a deaf ear to the messages I brought him from the Lord, and never did he ignore my counsel.

So I was overjoyed when he asked for my blessing on his intended marriage to my daughter, Hephzibah. His request did not come as a surprise. Nebiah and I had been witnessing this developing relationship between them for some time. We knew it would be a marriage of complementing strengths, of mutual love and respect, and of shared passion to honor the Lord in all things.

There was a huge celebration throughout the kingdom on Hezekiah and Hephzibah's wedding day. There was no question in anyone's mind that God was again showering His blessings on our king and the kingdom. And I thanked the Lord for one additional role He had granted me – to be the father-in-law of the king I loved so dearly.

For a while it seemed as if nothing could go wrong – our days were filled with joy. But during the fourteenth year of Hezekiah's reign, the armies of King Sennacherib of Assyria came to attack Judah.

~

16

PREPARING FOR AN ASSYRIAN INVASION

~

While Ahaz was king, Judah's wealth and resources were depleted because of the offerings demanded by the king of Assyria. An empty treasury held little interest for subsequent rulers of Assyria. So Judah was left alone, despite the fact the Assyrians controlled the regions surrounding the kingdom.

Hezekiah had no intention of making payments, but he knew Assyria would not ignore Judah forever. So, he sought an alliance with Sidon, Ascalon, Ekron, and Egypt in hopes that together they could keep the Assyrians at bay. Once King Sennacherib learned of this rebel alliance, however, he set out to destroy it.

He dispatched his army to attack Ascalon, followed by Sidon, and then Ekron. Each domain fell and was absorbed into the Assyrian kingdom. By that point, the alliance had broken down and everyone was left to fend for themselves. Sennacherib next turned his attention toward Judah. He knew Jerusalem was the most fortified city of the kingdom, so he began by attacking the other cities.

. . .

One by one, the cities of Judah were defeated by Assyria's military. Hezekiah knew once the fortified cities fell, Sennacherib would target Jerusalem. And if Jerusalem fell, all would be lost. Judah would be conquered, and our people would be scattered as captives into Assyrian cities.

Hezekiah consulted with officials and his military advisers and determined Jerusalem would not survive a prolonged siege. He needed to buy enough time to strengthen the city's defenses. I, together with the rest of his counselors, advised Hezekiah to give the Assyrian king an offering in order to buy the needed time.

The Assyrian forces had just captured the city of Lachish, and Sennacherib had temporarily taken up residence there. Hezekiah sent the king a message, apologizing for his failure to make payments, saying it was a disrespectful expression of rebellion on his part.

Hezekiah hoped his offer to resume sending tribute would diminish Sennacherib's thirst to conquer Judah and cause him to turn back – or at least slow his advance toward Jerusalem. Hezekiah's message read: "To the honorable king of Assyria, *I have done wrong. I will pay whatever tribute money you demand if you will only go away.*"[(1)]

The Assyrian king sent back a message to Hezekiah with his demand: "I will accept no less than ten tons of silver, and one ton of gold."[(2)]

Though the demand was outrageous, we all advised Hezekiah to make the payment. All the silver stored in the temple of the Lord and in the palace treasury was gathered. Even the gold inlaid on the doors and doorposts of the temple was stripped so we could meet the king's demand. Twenty-two oxen-drawn carts, protected by 1,000 of our fighting men, traveled for two days to deliver the silver and gold to the king.

. . .

But even before the oxen departed Jerusalem, Hezekiah ordered repairs to begin on the wall of the city. Once that was finished, construction on a second wall outside of the first was completed. The king also ordered the defensive terraces surrounding the City of David be reinforced.

Hezekiah knew one of our greatest vulnerabilities was our water supply, which comes from the Gihon Spring. The spring originates at the base of the hill on which the City of David is built. The spring's waters emerge from a cave, which in turn acts as a siphon on the eastern side of the city and, at the time, flowed from there into Jerusalem through channels in the Kidron Valley.

Knowing the Assyrians could easily dam the channels – leaving us with no access to water – Hezekiah redirected the water flow by building an underground tunnel beneath the City of David leading from the spring to a pool inside the walls of Jerusalem. It was an amazing engineering feat.

Two teams, starting at opposite ends and working toward the middle, began excavation of the 533-meter tunnel. It took four years to complete, which in the providence of Jehovah God, coincided with the time Sennacherib began his attacks on our fortified cities.

Once Hezekiah became aware that an Assyrian attack was imminent, he directed the above-ground access be capped off. Not only did this protect our water supply, but it also diminished the water available to the Assyrian forces.

Countless workers began manufacturing weapons and shields so all our people would be equipped for battle. Shifts worked around the clock – except on the Sabbath – until all the preparations were completed.

~

17

THE ASSYRIAN KING MOCKS THE LORD GOD

Hezekiah called all the people of Jerusalem to gather in the square at the city gate. He knew they were anxious because they had heard what the Assyrians had done to the people in the cities they had conquered.

The king offered them this encouragement: *"Be strong and courageous! Don't be afraid of the king of Assyria or his mighty army, for there is a power far greater on our side! The Assyrian king may have a great army, but they are just men. We have the Lord our God to help us and to fight our battles for us!"*[(1)]

The people calmed down – until they saw the mighty Assyrian army approaching from the south. They watched as a large fighting force, led by Assyrian General Rab-shakeh, made camp on the horizon just outside the City of David.

We soon learned Sennacherib was not with them. He was planning to march on the city of Libnah with another portion of his army before meeting up with Rab-shakeh here in Jerusalem. He had sent this force to camp outside our walls to intimidate us. It wasn't long before Rab-shakeh approached our city gate. He shouted so all the people could hear.

"I am General Rab-shakeh, personal representative of the great king of Assyria! *This is what our great king says to Hezekiah, king of Judah: 'What are you trusting in that makes you so confident? Do you think that mere words can substitute for military skill and strength? Which of your military allies will give you any backing against Assyria? Will Egypt? If you lean on Egypt, you will find it to be a stick that breaks into pieces. The pharaoh of Egypt is completely unreliable!*(2)

"'But perhaps you will say that you are trusting in the Lord your God. Surely you must realize what I and the other kings of Assyria before me have done to all the people of the earth! Were any of their gods able to rescue them from my power? Name just one time when any god anywhere was able to rescue his people from me!(3)

"'People of Judah, do not let Hezekiah fool you! Don't let him deceive you like this! I say it again – no god of any nation has ever yet been able to rescue his people from me or my ancestors. How much less will your God rescue you from my power!'"(4)

The general continued to mock the Lord God Jehovah and His servant Hezekiah by heaping one insult after another. Rab-shakeh spoke about our God in heaven as if He were one of the pagan gods made by human hands.

"King Hezekiah," General Rab-shakeh called out, *"I'll tell you what! My master, the king of Assyria, has said, 'I will strike a bargain with you. If you can find two thousand horsemen in your entire army, I will give you two thousand horses for them to ride on! With your tiny army, how can you think of challenging even the weakest contingent of my troops?'"*(5)

• • •

"People of Judah, don't listen to Hezekiah! This is what my king is offering to you: 'Make peace with me – open the gates and come out. Then I will allow each of you to continue eating from your own garden and drinking from your own well. Then I will arrange to take you to another land like this one – a country with bountiful harvests of grain and wine, bread and vineyards, olive trees and honey – a land of plenty. Choose life instead of death!'"(6)

When the general finished, he returned to the Assyrian camp. Our people silently waited for their king to respond. Hezekiah tore his clothes, put on sackcloth, and entered the temple of the Lord to pray.

Before doing so, he sent me this message: "Isaiah, *this is a day of trouble, insult, and disgrace. It is like when a child is ready to be born, but the mother has no strength to deliver it. But perhaps the Lord our God has heard the words of the Assyrian messenger defying* Him and blaspheming His name. What would the Lord God have me say to the Assyrians?"(7)

The Lord had already given me His reply.

"King Hezekiah, *this is what the Lord says: 'Do not be disturbed by the blasphemous speech against Me from the Assyrian king's messenger. Listen! I Myself will make sure that the king will receive a report from Assyria telling him that he is needed at home. Then I will make him want to return to his land, where I will have him killed with a sword.'"*(8)

For the next several days, the Assyrian army remained in their encampment making their preparations to attack us – and we waited on our God!

~

18

THE LORD GOD JEHOVAH WILL NOT BE MOCKED

A few days later, as the morning sun rose, our lookouts brought word the Assyrian army was gone. They had left in the middle of the night. People across the city began to shout with joy. Praises to God for His deliverance poured from their lips – but their jubilation was short-lived.

Later that morning, Hezekiah's spies reported that General Rab-shakeh had only withdrawn his troops temporarily. The general had received word the army led by King Sennacherib was being attacked by the king of Egypt. Rab-shakeh's army had gone to assist in the fight.

Hezekiah received a letter around midday from Sennacherib's general that read: "Do not be deceived into thinking I have withdrawn in defeat. I will return – and when I do, it will be with my full force!"

The next day the Lord gave me this message He had spoken against the Assyrian king: *"Whom have you been defying and ridiculing? Against whom did you raise your voice? At whom did you look with such haughty eyes? It was the Holy One of Israel!*

"By your messengers you have defied the Lord. You have said, 'With my many chariots I have conquered the highest mountains – yes, the remotest peaks of Lebanon. I have cut down its tallest cedars and its finest cypress trees. I have reached its farthest heights and explored its deepest forests. I have dug wells in many foreign lands and refreshed myself with their water. With the sole of my foot, I stopped up all the rivers of Egypt!'

"But have you not heard? I decided this long ago. Long ago I planned it, and now I am making it happen. I planned for you to crush fortified cities into heaps of rubble.

That is why their people have so little power and are so frightened and confused. They are as weak as grass, as easily trampled as tender green shoots.

"But I know you well – where you stay and when you come and go. I know the way you have raged against Me. And because of your raging against Me and your arrogance, which I have heard for Myself, I will put My hook in your nose and My bit in your mouth. I will make you return by the same road on which you came."(1)

Immediately, I went to the Great Hall to find Hezekiah and tell him what the Lord said.

Several weeks later, the Assyrian forces reappeared on the horizon outside the City of David. But this time, it was the combined forces of the Assyrian army, fresh on the heels of their defeat of the Egyptian army.

Again, I went before Hezekiah and brought him this message: *"This is what the Lord says about the king of Assyria: 'His armies will not enter Jerusalem to shoot their arrows. They will not march outside its gates with their shields or build banks of earth against its walls. The king will not enter this city. For My own honor and for the sake of My servant David, I will defend it.'"*[2]

Hezekiah sent word to all the people: "Watch and see the deliverance of the Lord!"

Throughout the night, Hezekiah remained in the temple of the Lord praying for the deliverance of his people. Little did he, or anyone else, know what the Lord was doing as many of us joined him in prayer.

As the sun rose, we heard shouts from the Assyrian camp. But they were not shouts of war – they were shouts of confusion! About 185,000 soldiers had come down with a plague overnight and were dead. The handful remaining were surrounded by dead corpses. Fear and panic spread throughout their camp.

We watched as Sennacherib, Rab-shakeh, and the few remaining officers tried to bring order to their greatly reduced ranks. But even from a distance we could tell they were all afraid. Within minutes, the order was given to break camp and quickly depart to the south. They didn't even take time to bury their dead.

Shouts of joy again broke out across the city. Hezekiah led us in a week-long season of praise and thanksgiving before our God. As always, He had been true to His Word. He had defended our city and defeated our enemy, and we didn't raise a hand. All glory and honor were due Him – and Him alone!

Never again was Hezekiah threatened by the Assyrians. God had fought for us. Many years later, I learned Sennacherib had returned home to Nineveh and remained there … until he was killed by two of his sons. Our God will not be mocked!

19

"SET YOUR AFFAIRS IN ORDER."

~

The entire kingdom was aware King Hezekiah had no heir to the throne. My daughter, Hephzibah, had not yet borne him children during their three years of marriage. Before, everyone's thoughts had been preoccupied with the Assyrian threats; but now, without those to distract us, the lack of an heir was a growing concern.

No one was more anxious than Hezekiah and my daughter. My precious wife and I continued to reassure them God would be faithful to provide an heir in His timing, but He had not given me a specific message of assurance for them. It soon became obvious what a toll worry was taking on them both emotionally and physically.

But I also noticed how quickly Hezekiah tired – much too fast for a man in his late thirties, even one who bore the responsibilities of a king. I suggested he talk to his physicians and see if they had a remedy to help him regain his energy and strength.

. . .

Unfortunately, his physicians were little help. They could not find anything wrong with him physically, and none of their remedies worked. I prayed that Jehovah Rapha would strengthen His servant and take away whatever was afflicting his body.

But as the weeks passed, there was no improvement. As a matter of fact, sores began to develop on Hezekiah's body. One night as I cried out to God, the Lord gave me a message for the king. But like many others over the years, it was not a message I looked forward to sharing.

When I arrived at the Great Hall the next morning, Hezekiah was still in his bed chambers. Apparently, he had not felt strong enough to get out of bed. I went to his room and found him surrounded by my daughter and several physicians. They all looked worried, but no one seemed to know what to do.

"My king," I began, *"I have come to you with a message from the Lord. He says, 'Set your affairs in order, for you are going to die. You will not recover from this illness.'"*(1)

I heard the physicians gasp. They started to contradict me but realized they could not challenge the word of the Lord. My daughter looked at me in horror as tears streamed down her cheeks. Hezekiah turned his face away from me toward the wall and prayed out loud.

"Remember, O Lord," he prayed, *"how I have always tried to be faithful to You and do what is pleasing in Your sight."*(2)

Then he broke down and began to weep bitterly.

My daughter cried out, "No, father! That can't be right! Surely Jehovah God will not let my husband die!"

. . .

I had wrestled with God over the message throughout the night, saying: "This king has sought to honor You in word and deed with all his heart. He has not retreated from the task You have given him. He has led Your people to honor You and worship you. He has never once turned to the right or the left. In Your mercy, Oh Lord, heal Hezekiah and grant him life ... not death."

But I had not sensed any release from the message God had given me. And now my heart was broken as I listened to Hezekiah and my daughter weep. My heart was broken for our people who would soon hear the news about their king. My heart was broken for my own pain. My heart was broken that I had been the one to deliver the message.

Though I knew God understood our pain, I questioned why He would not answer our prayer. Though I knew God in His infinite wisdom knew what was best for us all, I questioned why in His sovereignty He would not make this right. Though I knew God loved Hezekiah even more than I did, I questioned why His answer reflected so little compassion.

Dealing with my own emotions, plus watching this young couple's agony, I suddenly felt like I was drowning in sorrow. I needed to escape for a while and find a place where I could be alone with God.

As I walked outside into the courtyard, the warmth of the morning sun touched my face. It felt as if God were embracing me and giving me comfort. I felt Him draw me close and say: "Go back to Hezekiah and give him this message!"

~

20

TEN DEGREES BACKWARD

~

I walked back into Hezekiah's chamber and announced to him and Hephzibah: *"This is what the Lord, the God of your ancestor David, says. 'I have heard your prayer and seen your tears. I will heal you, and three days from now you will get out of bed and go to the temple of the Lord. I will add fifteen years to your life.'"*(1)

I called to the servants waiting just outside my son-in-law's chamber. *"Make an ointment from figs and spread it over the sores on his body."*(2)

The physicians again looked at me with disbelief, but just like before they knew better than to contradict the prophet of the Lord. Hezekiah cautiously asked, *"What sign will the Lord give to prove that He will heal me and that I will go to the temple of the Lord three days from now?"*(3)

"Throughout your days," I told him, "you have seen the faithfulness of the Lord your God. He has delivered you from the hands of your enemies. He has prospered you and granted you His favor in all your dealings. Whatever He has promised, He has accomplished. He does not lie. But now you ask for a sign from Him?"

"Your words that I am to set my affairs in order still echo in my ears," Hezekiah replied. "And now you tell me God has granted me fifteen additional years. How am I to know which statement is the one true message from the Lord our God?"

"This is the sign that the Lord will give you to prove He will do as He promised," I answered. *"Would you like the sundial* in the courtyard of the temple *to go forward ten steps or backward ten steps?"*[4]

He said, *"The shadow always moves forward. Make it go backward instead."*[5]

"I will ask God to do as you have requested," I replied.

And so, the Lord did. The shadow moved backward ten degrees that afternoon and then resumed its forward motion adding forty minutes to that day. God who created all things – including time – altered its natural course that one day to make it a 24-hour and 40-minute day to give Hezekiah a sign!

Each day afterward, Hezekiah regained more strength. By the end of three days, his skin was clear and his sores were gone. On the third day, he got out of bed and entered the temple of the Lord – just as God had promised!

"Lord, You have restored my health and have allowed me to live!" Hezekiah prayed. *"You have rescued me from death and have forgiven all my sins. You have healed me. I will sing Your praises with instruments every day of my life in Your temple."*[6]

. . .

News of what God had done for Hezekiah spread throughout the lands. Judah's people rejoiced and praised God. Gifts began to pour into Jerusalem from kings of other nations, expressing their thanks to God for His compassionate mercy to Hezekiah.

The kings also sent valuable presents as expressions of their high esteem for my son-in-law. His wealth grew, as did his treasury. But there was still one thing he lacked. Nebiah and I knew all too well the cry of his and my daughter's hearts.

Not long after Hezekiah had been healed, God answered that prayer as well.

As he shared with me that Hephzibah was pregnant, Hezekiah told me it was a gift that was even more precious to him than his own life.

When the time was completed, all of Judah celebrated the birth of a son – an heir to the throne! The festivities were even more grand than the party marking Hezekiah's recovery. The people rejoiced that their beloved King Hezekiah now had a son who would reign after him. A son who would continue to lead the people to honor Jehovah God.

Nebiah and I were grandparents! Our hearts were overflowing! I was going to have the opportunity to nurture my grandson just as I had nurtured Hezekiah when he was a boy. It was hard to believe that less than a year earlier, we were mourning our son-in-law's imminent death; but today, we were joining him and our daughter in thanksgiving for a new life.

Hezekiah and Hephzibah named their son Manasseh in honor of Hezekiah's younger brother, whose life had tragically been taken by Ahaz. The name means "God has made me forget all the troubles of my father's house." It was a most fitting name for Hezekiah to give to his son.

. . .

Everyone was so joyful ... but little did we know what the birth of this son would mean for us all in the days ahead.

21

A KING'S PRIDE

~

The Lord occasionally called on me to leave Jerusalem and travel into different parts of the wilderness east of the city. It was often during those times of prayer and fasting that He gave me messages for His people. After extending Hezekiah's life, the Lord seemed to be leading me out into the wilderness more often.

Throughout that time, the Lord God Jehovah continued to bless the reign of Hezekiah. The king had to build additional treasury buildings to hold the accumulation of silver, gold, precious stones, and spices, as well as for the shields and other items of value.

He also constructed more storehouses for the plentiful harvests of grain and the new wine and olive oil they produced. Many new stalls were built to accommodate the great increase in his herds and flocks. By the will and grace of God, he succeeded in everything he did.

. . .

But throughout my times in the wilderness, the Lord continued to remind me that Judah would one day be conquered just as the northern kingdom of Israel had been. Our people would be taken into captivity and scattered like the people of Israel. The threat might come from Assyria, or it could come from another quarter – the growing kingdom of Babylon.

The Lord showed me that kingdoms come, and kingdoms go – only the Lord God Jehovah remains. He permits kings and kingdoms to rise and fall – and through them His will is accomplished. Though the people of Judah may be scattered in captivity and Jerusalem destroyed, the Lord will protect a remnant – one He will use to rebuild His city.

As I was returning to Jerusalem from one of those times in the wilderness, what looked like a royal delegation passed me on the road. Evidently, they had come from Jerusalem and were now traveling toward Jericho. They seemed to be in a hurry, as if they were taking news back to the one who had sent them.

I didn't know for certain, but their flamboyant attire and manner made me think they were Babylonians. I decided to go to the Great Hall to see Hezekiah before stopping to see Nebiah. Upon my arrival I asked him, "My king, *what did those men want? Where were they from?*"(1)

"They were envoys from King Baladan of Babylon," he replied. "They arrived unexpectedly and brought gifts from their king. Baladan had heard of my sickness and recovery, and he sent them to express his best wishes."

Hezekiah was so in awe that the Babylonian king would honor him in such a way, he became prideful. He forgot the source of all his blessings and chose to impress the Babylonian king by showing the envoys the great wealth of Judah. He flaunted everything in the treasury buildings, the storehouses, and the armory.

. . .

There was nothing in his palace or the kingdom that he did not reveal. His pride blinded him to the reality that his boasts were exposing the kingdom to great threat from the most powerful empire in the region.

My heart was quickly burdened for what he had done. "My king," I said, *"listen to this message from the Lord Almighty: 'The time is coming when everything you have – all the treasures stored up by your ancestors – will be carried off to Babylon. Nothing will be left!*[2] *Some of your own descendants will be taken away into exile. They will become eunuchs who will serve in the palace of Babylon's king.'"*[3]

Hezekiah's response took me by surprise: *"This message you have given me from the Lord is good."*[4]

Hezekiah had heard me say his descendants would be taken away. So, he surmised the captivity would not occur during his reign – rather, there would be peace and security for the remainder of his lifetime. Our king had become more concerned about his personal fate than the fate of his people.

It was the first time I had ever been ashamed of this one who had sat at my knee and earnestly taken in the truth and promises of the Lord. Until now, I had seen him seek the Lord on behalf of his people and seek their welfare above his own. But today, I had seen a different Hezekiah – and my heart was broken.

In the months that followed, I repeatedly thought back to the day the Lord had extended Hezekiah's life. I remembered how he had prayed for God's mercy, and how I had interceded on his behalf. I began to wonder if those prayers God granted had taken us down a road that wasn't God's best for His people.

. . .

What if God's best had been for Hezekiah to die at that time? But if he had died, who would now be king? Manasseh had not yet been conceived in my daughter's womb. And yet, what kind of king would he be? I was seeing more of Ahaz in the boy than I was seeing Hezekiah – at least the Hezekiah I had known up until now.

I cried out to God for mercy – but I knew difficult days were ahead.

22

A KING IS HONORED

Though the Lord showed me defeat, destruction, and captivity lay ahead in our immediate future, He also assured me His deliverance would one day follow. I heard a voice call out, "Shout!"

"What should I shout?"[(1)] I asked.

An angel said, *"Shout that people are like the grass that dies away. Their beauty fades as quickly as the beauty of flowers in a field. The grass withers and the flowers fade, but the word of our God stands forever.*[(2)]

"Make a highway for the Lord through the wilderness. Make a straight, smooth road through the desert for our God. Fill the valleys and level the hills. Straighten the curves and smooth the rough spots. For the glory of the Lord will be revealed, and all the people will see it!"[(3)]

. . .

It was the middle of the night. I couldn't sleep, so I left Nebiah in bed and went into another room to pray. That was when I heard the message from the Lord as I was praising Him for His endless goodness, comfort, and assurance. Suddenly, there was a loud knock on the main door of our chambers.

It was Hephzibah! "Father, my husband is asking for you. You must come quickly!"

I followed Nebiah and my daughter into Hezekiah's bed chamber. The king was surrounded by his physicians and several of his officials. Out of the corner of my eye, I saw Manasseh watching from a corner of the room. The king was barely able to speak above a whisper, and even that was with great effort.

"Come closer, Isaiah," he said. "There are but a few grains of sand remaining in the hourglass of my life, and I have something important to say to you. God has been faithful to grant me every day of the fifteen additional years He promised, and I desire to use this last day wisely.

"Since the days of my youth, you have been my teacher, my conscience, and my wise counselor. If I have done any good in my reign as king, it was because you have been right there beside me pointing me in the right direction. And where I have done wrong, it has been because I failed to heed your counsel.

"In a matter of moments, I will take my last breath and your grandson will become your king. He has not sought you out like I did at his age. He has been content to watch from a distance. But I need you to promise me that you will seek him out. He may not know to seek your wise counsel and the messages you carry from the Lord, but you must make sure he hears from you, nonetheless."

. . .

"I have promised God I will do so," I replied, "and now I promise you as well, my king. Rest peacefully in the presence of the God you have faithfully followed and obeyed."

When I turned to go comfort Manasseh, he had gone. He wasn't there to hear his mother cry out when Hezekiah took his last breath. Two of Hezekiah's officials immediately left to go find our new king and tell him his father had died.

All of Judah mourned and honored their beloved king. I, together with his other officials, had assisted Hezekiah in preplanning his own funeral arrangements. He had wanted to lead his people in death just as he had done in life. He had not wanted the responsibility to fall upon Hephzibah or his twelve-year-old son.

Hezekiah's body was buried in the upper area of the royal cemetery near those of King David and King Solomon. It was the section of the cemetery reserved for the great kings of Judah. There was no question among the people that Hezekiah had earned the right to be buried in that place of honor.

To his credit, Manasseh stood beside his mother and presided over his father's funeral arrangements with a strength and maturity that surpassed his years. He declared the thirty days immediately following his father's death to be a time of mourning throughout the land. He sat in the presence of his father's counselors and heeded our advice.

We counseled Manasseh to continue in the ways of his father. We encouraged him to allow the people to complete their days of mourning before enacting any changes. The time would allow them to grieve their former king and begin to embrace their new king.

• • •

Numerous people questioned Manasseh's ability to rule wisely because of his age, but those of us who counseled his father would do the same for him. Throughout the days of mourning, he heeded our advice without exception. The days were peaceful and calm.

But the Lord quickened my heart. A storm was coming, and it would come swiftly. The day after the month of mourning concluded … the storm arrived!

~

23

A NEW KING, A NEW DAY

I was eighty-eight years old when my twelve-year-old grandson became my king. I never expected to live longer than the three kings I had served before him. By His grace, God has given me the health and strength to serve Him faithfully, even now in my old age.

I have seen kings at their best – and at their worst. I have seen people follow their kings at their best – and at their worst. I have seen our kings and our people love God with their whole hearts – and I have seen them turn away from Him. I have seen our kingdom enjoy the great blessings of God – and I have seen us experience His wrath.

I have seen God single-handedly defeat our enemies, and I have seen Him permit them to overrun and defeat us. I have seen the temple and the surrounding hills cleansed so that we might worship God as He has chosen, and I have seen them desecrated by pagan idols and graven images. I have seen the nation exalted in righteousness, and I have seen it destroyed in wickedness.

• • •

And yet, it always amazes me how easily our hearts can be turned away from God. We can so easily forget His blessings from the past and His promises for the future. We can so easily be deceived into thinking our ways are better than His ways and our thoughts are better than His thoughts. Sadly, such was the case with my grandson.

The day after the mourning period for Hezekiah concluded, Manasseh called all the officials and counselors to appear before him in the Great Hall. He thanked us for our service to his father and for our service to him throughout the days of mourning. But then he told us he no longer required our service.

"Many of you men are now well advanced in years," he announced. "And all of you are very tired. It is time for you to enjoy a well-deserved rest. You have long served your king and the kingdom, and now it is time for you to allow others to do the same."

"My king," I replied, "perhaps it would be wise to allow us to assist your new officials as they assume their roles, so they might benefit from the wisdom we have gleaned through the years and be better able to counsel you well."

"Thank you, grandfather," he answered sarcastically, "for always thinking of my best interest, but those I have selected to serve in my court already have my utmost trust and respect. They have already demonstrated a wisdom and understanding that aligns with my thinking. They truly do not require any assistance from you!"

"Your majesty," I continued, "might we inquire as to who these new counselors are?"

"You most definitely may inquire," he answered. "As a matter of fact, they are entering the hall even as we speak."

. . .

We all turned to watch as they approached – there were only a few men I recognized. Many of them were not much older than our king, and those I recognized I knew to be ne'er-do-wells. I feared there wasn't one herald of wise counsel among them.

My daughter had watched silently as her son made his pronouncement, but now seeing how events were unfolding, she spoke up. "Your majesty, perhaps your grandfather's counsel is worthy to reconsider. These young men with their obvious strength and energy could benefit from some time with those who have gone before them."

Manasseh was visibly annoyed. "Thank you, mother. But I must ask that you leave the decisions on ruling our nation to me, the one who has been ordained by your God to do so. It is a new day in Judah. We will not be restricted by the old ways. We must become more like our neighbors, the Assyrians and the Babylonians, if we are going to prosper in the days ahead. We need new thinking, and these men will provide it to me.

"And in the future, Mother, I would ask that you refrain from attempting to counsel me in my Great Hall. As a matter of fact, I would ask that you and those who are no longer serving as my officials leave the hall so I can meet with my new counselors!"

All of us looked at one another, not quite sure what we should do.

Seeing our hesitation, the king continued. "But if you are unable to find your way out of the hall, I can always have my guards show you the way!"

With that, we all turned and walked out. I prayed God would show us what He would have us do next.

24

THE ONE WHOSE COMING IS PROMISED

~

I tossed and turned in bed that night as I worried about what was about to happen in Judah. My spirit was in turmoil, and nothing could put my mind at ease. All of a sudden, I heard familiar voices. I strained to hear what they were saying but couldn't quite make out the words.

I carefully rose out of bed so as not to wake Nebiah and went to the door of our bed chamber. The voices seemed to be coming from the other room.

As I stepped through the door, I was surprised to find myself in a large, open space – and not the room outside our bed chamber! I was immediately washed in a light as bright as the noonday sun. It took a few minutes for my eyes to adjust, but I continued to listen to the voices.

As everything came into focus, I realized I had been here before. This was the place I had heard Jehovah God ask, "*Who will go for Us?*"[(1)] But this time there wasn't a multitude of people standing around Him. I saw the shapes of only two people off in the distance. Though I could not see their faces, their voices were as clear as if I were standing right beside them.

All at once, I saw movement as if they were turning to look at me – but I still could not distinguish their features. However, I could tell One of them was speaking to me. His was the voice I recognized. He was the One who had told me to go and tell His people. I listened carefully so I would hear His every word: "You are the messenger I have sent to My people. How have My people responded to My message?"

I answered, "*My work all seems so useless!* There are some who have turned to You and followed You, but there are still others who seem intent on turning away from You. King Hezekiah was intent on obeying You and following You. But now his son, Manasseh, is even more intent on disobeying You and leading Your people to abandon You. *I have spent my strength for nothing and to no purpose at all."*(2)

Jehovah God immediately corrected me. "*Forget all that – it is nothing compared to what I am going to do. For I am about to do a brand-new thing. I will make a pathway through the wilderness for My people to come home. Yes, I will make springs in the desert, so that My people can be refreshed. I have made them for Myself, and they will someday honor Me before the whole world."*(3)

Next, the other One – the One I knew was the Messiah – spoke up, saying, *"He who formed Me in My mother's womb to be His servant, who commissioned Me to bring His people back to Him, has honored Me and given Me strength."*(4)

Jehovah God continued, "*You will do more than restore the people of Israel back to Me. I will make You a Light to the Gentiles, and You will bring My salvation to the ends of the earth.*(5)

"I am the Lord, the Redeemer and Holy One of Israel, and I say to the One who will be despised and rejected by a nation, to the One who is a Servant of rulers:

Kings will stand at attention when You pass by. Princes will bow low because the Lord has chosen You. I, the faithful Lord, the Holy One of Israel, choose You.[6]

"Isaiah, record these words: '*My Servant will prosper; He will be highly exalted. Many will be amazed when they see Him – beaten and bloodied, so disfigured one would scarcely know He was a Person. And when He returns, He will again startle many nations. Kings will stand speechless in His presence. For they will see what they have previously refused to see, and they will understand what they would not hear.*'"[7]

I was standing not only in the presence of the Holy One of Israel, but I was also standing before the One who will bring salvation to all the earth. I fell prostrate before them and cried out: "Holy, holy, holy!"

~

25

A MESSAGE OF SALVATION

After a while, I asked: "Lord, *who will believe Your message? To whom will You reveal Your saving power?*"[1]

He answered, "My Servant will grow up in their presence like a tender green shoot, sprouting from a root in a dry and sterile ground. There will be nothing beautiful or majestic about His appearance, nothing to attract them to Him. He will be despised and rejected – a Man of sorrows, acquainted with the bitterest grief. They will turn their backs on Him and look the other way as He passes by.[2]

"Yet it will be their weaknesses He carries; it will be their sorrows that weigh Him down. They will think His troubles are a punishment from Me for His own sins! But, rather, He will be wounded and crushed for their sins. He will be beaten that they might have peace. He will be whipped so they may be healed.[3]

. . .

"All of them have strayed away like sheep. They have left My path to follow their own, just like your King Manasseh. Yet, on the One I send will I lay the guilt and sins of them all![4]

"My Son whom I send will be oppressed and treated harshly; yet, He will not say a word. He will be led as a Lamb to the slaughter. And as a sheep is silent before the shearers, He will not open His mouth. From prison and trial, they will lead Him away to His death.[5]

"But who among the people will realize that He is dying for their sins – He is suffering their punishment? He will have done no wrong and never will have deceived anyone. He will be buried like a criminal and placed in a rich man's grave. But it will all have been My good plan to crush Him and fill Him with grief.[6]

"And because of what He has experienced, My Righteous Servant will make it possible for many to be counted righteous, for He will bear all their sins. I will give Him the honors of One who is mighty and great, because He exposed Himself to death and bore the sins of many![7]

"Now, return to the people and tell them, 'Fear not, Jerusalem; you will not live in shame for much longer. Enlarge your house and build an addition. For you will soon be bursting at the seams. Your descendants will include other nations and their cities. The shame of your youth and the sorrows of your disobedience that led to your widowhood will be remembered no more.'[8]

"Tell them, 'The Holy One whom I send will come as the Bridegroom and He will restore you back to Me. Though you abandoned Me, turn to Him and I will take you back. Your sins will be forgiven and forgotten, and you will be clothed in His righteousness.' I, the Lord, have spoken."

. . .

Immediately, the place was filled with a great multitude of people, lifting their voices in a chorus, "Holy, holy, holy is the Lord Almighty!" The foundations began to shake as they sang.

The next thing I knew, the shaking had stopped and everything was quiet. I opened my eyes to discover I was lying in my bed. The morning sun was beginning to rise. Nebiah was standing beside our bed looking down at me.

"Husband, Jehovah God has given you another message for His people, hasn't He?"

"Yes, He has!" I replied. "And it is the greatest message He could possibly give. It is a message of the salvation that will come. Manasseh may lead our people to turn away from God once again, as some of our fathers have done before him, but that will not change the fact that a new day is coming.

"The Lord Almighty will spread a wonderful feast in Jerusalem for everyone around the world. It will be a delicious feast. In that day, He will remove the cloud of gloom, the shadow of death that hangs over the earth. He will swallow up death forever! The Sovereign Lord will wipe away all tears.[9]

"He will remove forever all insults and mockery against His land and people. In that day, the people will proclaim, 'This is our God. We trusted in Him, and He saved us. Let us rejoice in the salvation He brings! For the Lord's good hand rests upon us!'[10]

"Nebiah, Jehovah God has given me a message for all generations. It is a message of hope. It is a message of salvation. It is a message about the One who is to come. I pray our people will not turn away from our God – but we have His assurance that even if they do, we will one day rejoice in the blessings that only His salvation can bring! And I can't possibly think of any better news!"

~

26

THE PAGAN SHRINES AND ALTARS RETURN

I wept as I watched Manasseh undo all his father had accomplished. I could only imagine the sorrow his actions were bringing to Jehovah God. Within the first year of his reign, my grandson had rebuilt all the pagan shrines his father had destroyed.

Each time I attempted to deliver a message from the Lord, I encountered the ridicule of his officials and the rebuff of the king. Manasseh's heart was not only closed to what I had to say, but he would fly into a rage against me – and against Jehovah God. After the last occasion, he ordered that I never again be permitted entry into the Great Hall.

It took no time before the streets and hills, as well as the temple, were dotted with pagan priests, mediums, and psychics. The priests of the Lord were ordered to leave the temple. Asherah poles were again raised, and images of Baal appeared throughout the landscape. A cloud of evil blanketed Jerusalem!

• • •

Manasseh's officials wasted no time in finding him a suitable wife. Meshullemeth was the daughter of a sorcerer named Harez, who had been able to keep his witchcraft hidden from Hezekiah. She was a few years older than the king and in her prime childbearing years. The king's counselors wanted their young monarch to father an heir as soon as possible. Meshullemeth could also help school the king and his future heir in the darker pagan arts she had learned from her father.

Hephzibah's attempts to discourage her son from marrying Meshullemeth were rejected, and she, too, was soon cut off from having any contact with him. Evil permeated the palace and had taken control of the king's thoughts and actions.

Meshullemeth gave birth during the first year of Manasseh's reign. Confident he would soon have an heir, the king ordered a great celebration take place throughout the kingdom. However, when the baby turned out to be a girl – a daughter they named Naamah – he demanded the celebration cease. He was so furious the child was not a son, he would have absolutely nothing to do with her.

A plague swept through our land the following year. The Lord did not give me any indication He had sent it as a reprimand for His people. I knew His punishment was still to come. But even if He had not sent the plague, I knew He had permitted it because of the evil that had overtaken His people.

No one was immune from the effects of the plague. One evening I discovered Nebiah lying on the floor of our quarters in the palace. She was delirious, her pallor was yellow, and her body was racked with relentless cold shivers.

The palace physicians were overwhelmed with sick patients and offered little consolation or assistance. The fever did not discriminate. It afflicted those in the fields, as well as those in the palace. It attacked both the old and the young. I soon learned that Manasseh's daughter, Naamah, had also taken sick.

Within a matter of days, my precious Nebiah and little Naamah both died. Though I had been permitted little contact with my great-granddaughter, I was overcome with grief over both deaths.

The pagan priests began to offer sacrifices night and day to beg Baal to take away the fever. But, to no surprise, their efforts yielded no results. As the death toll began to rise, Manasseh's officials counseled him to offer human sacrifices to satisfy Baal and stop the fever. Instead, he did something that was contrary to his nature. He sent word for me to come to the Great Hall. The Lord told me to come out of mourning and go.

When I arrived, the king said, "Isaiah, the priests of Baal have offered sacrifices to him and pleaded with him to take away the plague, but he has proven himself to either be unwilling or unable to do so. My officials have counseled me to sacrifice children to the gods in order to quench their thirst for blood. But I have decided to try something else instead.

"If your God Jehovah, the God of my father, is truly who you say He is, He can take away the plague. Ask your God to do so, and if He does, I will worship Him."

Though I had learned to be cautious of my grandson's promises, I was still somewhat encouraged by this statement. "King Manasseh," I replied, "by your word I will do as you have asked. But when Jehovah God turns away the plague, do not fail to heed the promise you have made!"

I walked out of the Great Hall and out of the palace into the city. I continued through the city gate, across the valley, and to the hill overlooking the city. When I had climbed high enough to see the entire city, I lifted my arms and cried out to God.

. . .

"Lord, prove today You are the God of Israel. Remove this plague from the city and show Your people and this king that You alone are the One who is worthy to be worshiped. Just as You have done for Your people many times before, show them Your majesty."

By the next morning, everyone who had been sick no longer had a fever. Jehovah God had healed our people and removed the plague. I immediately made my way to the entry doors of the Great Hall.

27

THE EVIL INCREASES

As I attempted to enter the Great Hall, my grandson sent word to me through his guards: "Go away, Isaiah, and do not return to my chambers. Our god Baal has removed the plague. Do not bother me about your God anymore!"

I knew the king could not truly believe this, but for whatever reason he had hardened his heart, like the pharaoh of Egypt, and refused to worship the Lord our God.

Ever since Nebiah died, I tended to stay out in the hills for longer periods of time. There was no one waiting for me to return home anymore. Our sons had long ago moved away to other parts of the kingdom, and our daughter, Queen Hephzibah, had died of a broken heart soon after the death of her mother. In many respects, the queen had become a prisoner in her own palace – unloved by her son and deeply wounded by his actions.

. . .

As the days passed, Manasseh fell further and further into the pit of darkness. His practice of fortune-telling was well-known throughout the city. Some said he could inspect the livers of sheep sacrificed on pagan altars and know the will of the gods.

Entrails of sacrificed sheep were brought to the Great Hall by the cartload for the king to examine. He had become consumed by the practice, and the smell of rotting animal flesh permeated the palace. It gave me a hint of how repulsive this behavior must be in the nostrils of Jehovah God.

At the same time, Queen Meshullemeth was teaching him the practice of witchcraft. Through fortune-telling he was attempting to see into the future, and now through witchcraft he was attempting to cast spells against his enemies. Over time, his perception of who his enemies were became more distorted. I was certain I was on that list.

Meshullemeth gave birth to another baby daughter during the third year of Manasseh's reign. This time the king was so enraged, he immediately had the baby thrown into the fires in the valley of the son of Hinnom as a sacrifice to Baal.

I would never have believed any king of Judah could be more evil than King Ahaz. But now I was witnessing his grandson – and mine – doing more wickedness than I ever could have imagined. And I knew the Lord's anger was being roused.

Then Manasseh had a carved idol made and placed in the temple of the Lord. He set it in the very place God had told Solomon: *"I have chosen this place for making sacrifices to Me. I will listen to every prayer made in this place, for I have chosen this temple and set it apart to be My home forever."*[1]

. . .

The Lord said to me, "*Tell Manasseh that thus says the Lord: 'Your hands are the hands of murderers, and your fingers are filthy with sin. Your mouth is full of lies, and your lips are tainted with corruption.*[2]

"You spend your time and energy spinning evil plans that end up in deadly actions. All your activity is filled with sin. Violence is your trademark. Your feet run to do evil, and you rush to commit murder. Wherever you go, misery and destruction follow you.

"That is why I will not punish those who injure you. For your sins are piled up before Me and testify against you. Your sins have cut you off from Me. Because of your sin, I have turned away and will not listen anymore.

"Weep, you people of Judah! Shave your heads in sorrow, for the children you love will be snatched away, and you will never see them again. They will be exiled to distant lands."

I passed by the temple as I returned to the city. Manasseh was outside presenting a sacrifice on his blasphemous altar to his pagan god. He could hide from me behind the doors of the Great Hall, but now he was standing right before me. The Lord told me: "This is the time to confront him with My message!"

Without hesitation, I called out, "King Manasseh, thus says the Lord of hosts." I then told him what the Lord had said, concluding with "… they will be exiled to distant lands."

When I finished, Manasseh called out to his guards. "Arrest this false prophet and take him in shackles to the Great Hall to stand in judgment before me!"

~

28

"THERE WILL BE NO PEACE FOR THE WICKED."

I had been in this Great Hall many times throughout my life. I had stood beside my childhood friend and cousin Jotham, listening with interest to the commands and rulings of his father, King Uzziah. I again stood beside that same friend as his chief counselor when he was king.

I had stood in the presence of King Ahaz before he banished me from the palace. I had returned to serve my student, son-in-law, and king – Hezekiah – counseling him with the words of the Lord. But I had never stood in this Great Hall shackled in chains as a prisoner to be judged by the king. Even Ahaz, for all his wickedness, had known better than to judge God's prophet.

Manasseh sat before me on his elevated throne. His officials sat in two rows extending the length of the hall on either side of me. Guards stood behind me with weapons pointed in my direction.

. . .

My grandson was permitting his officials to mock and ridicule me, and they were enjoying it tremendously.

"Old man, we have grown tired of your threats and those of your God," one councilor said. "Manasseh is king over our land, and Baal is our god. This is a time for fresh thinking and new words from young men who have vision. This is not a time for us to listen to the old stories about a worn-out God from our past. He has grown feeble, just as you have!

"How dare you speak to our king as you just did in the city square! You are a stiff-necked old man, and your disrespect to our king is treason! You will bow before him and pledge to serve him from this day forward. Furthermore, you will denounce your God and declare to the people that Baal alone is god! Otherwise, by order of this council and your king, you will be put to death!"

The king stood to his feet and stared at me, his eyes filled with hatred. "Isaiah, what say you? Will you denounce your God and worship Baal? And will you now bow before me, turn from the things of the past, and follow me into the future?"

I could feel the Spirit of the Lord giving me the words to answer and the boldness to do so. "Your majesty, *I will tell you new things I have not mentioned before; secrets you have not yet heard. They are brand new, not things from the past. So you cannot say, 'We knew that all the time!'*(1)

"Members of the council, *I will tell you of things that are entirely new, for I know so well what traitors you are! You have been rebels from your earliest childhood, rotten through and through.*(2)

"The Holy One of Israel says, *'For My own sake and for the honor of My name, I will hold back My anger and not wipe you out. I will refine you in the furnace of suffering. I will rescue you for My sake – yes, for My own sake. That way the pagan nations will not be able to claim that their gods have conquered Me. I will not let them have My glory!'*(3)

"Thus says the Sovereign Lord, *'Listen to Me, O family of Jacob, Israel My chosen one! I alone am God, the First and the Last. It was My hand that laid the foundations of the earth. The palm of My right hand spread out the heavens above. I spoke and they came into being.*(4)

"He also says, *'I am the Lord your God who teaches you what is good and leads you along the paths you should follow. Oh, that you had listened to My commands! Then you would have had peace flowing like a gentle river and righteousness rolling like waves.*(5)

"'You would have become as numerous as the sands along the seashore – too many to count! There would have been no need for your destruction. But instead there will be no peace for the wicked!'(6) Thus says the Lord God Jehovah."

The council members rose to their feet, their faces contorted with anger and loathing. They looked as if they were ready to execute me.

The councilor who had spoken before said, "Your majesty, we will not listen to any more of this! Render your judgment upon him! The executioner is waiting at the door. Do not permit him to wait any longer!"

My grandson looked at me and said, "Isaiah, tomorrow at dawn you will be put to death at the hand of your executioner in the most horrifying manner we can devise. You will wish you had bowed before me this day. But before your executioner is finished – you will cry out to me for mercy!"

I had never seen such hostility and wickedness in a person's eyes as I saw in my grandson's. Evil had completely overtaken him.

. . .

"Guards, take him away!" he shouted.

29

"I WILL GIVE BEAUTY FOR ASHES."

I had never been in this part of the palace before. To my knowledge, the dungeon had rarely been used during the reigns of Manasseh's predecessors. But it appeared that my grandson used it often. The smell of death filled my nostrils.

The guards' torches illuminated every conceivable instrument of death and torture. We passed cells housing what I assumed were other prisoners. The faint torchlight revealed men either lying lifeless in a heap or burrowed into the corner of their cell. The sounds of death and dismay echoed throughout the prison.

The guards did not speak as they led me to my cell. When we arrived, they pushed me through the small, gated opening and locked it behind me. Darkness blanketed me as their torches faded into the distance.

I quickly realized the cell's five-foot ceiling prevented me from standing up. As my eyes adjusted to the darkness, I noticed it was a very small space. There was nothing to sit or lie down on – just the dirt floor of the cold, damp stone cave. I'm sure neither my grandson, nor anyone else, was concerned about my lack of comfort.

I found a spot where I could sit with my back against the stone wall. It was near the opening so I could breathe a little air. I closed my eyes and spoke to God for the first time since He told me to confront Manasseh.

"Lord, I am Your messenger. The words I spoke were the words You gave me. I pray You have found me faithful to You and to the task You set before me. I do not know everything tomorrow will bring, but I pray You will find me faithful to the very end. Show me clearly what You would have me do – and give me the faith and strength to finish well."

As I sat there in that dingy cell with my eyes closed, I was suddenly transported to the great room in the heavens where Jehovah God had brought me twice before. This time, there was only One standing before me. He looked at me with compassion as He said, *"The Spirit of the Sovereign Lord is upon Me, because He has appointed Me to bring good news to the poor. He has sent Me to comfort the brokenhearted and to announce that captives will be released, and prisoners will be freed.*[1]

"He has sent Me to tell those who mourn that the time of the Lord's favor has come, and with it, the day of God's anger against their enemies. To all who mourn, He will give beauty for ashes, joy instead of mourning, praise instead of despair. For the Lord has planted them like strong and graceful oaks for His own glory.[2]

"And Isaiah, that is not only true when the Father's time comes to pass for Me to go to earth, it is also true today – and it is true for you! Through Me, He will give you beauty for ashes, joy instead of mourning, and praise instead of despair!

. . .

"You have remained faithful to the end, and I will be right there with you as you walk through these final hours. I will not leave you nor forsake you. Though you have been despised, hated, and rebuffed by all, you will be a joy to future generations for I will make you so. The Lord delights in you and will claim you as His own.

"The day is coming when I will create a new heaven and a new earth – so wonderful no one will even think about the old ones anymore. Be glad; rejoice forever in My creation. And look! I will create Jerusalem as a place of happiness and her people will be a source of joy.

"I will rejoice in Jerusalem and delight in My people. And the sound of weeping and crying will be heard no more. Isaiah, though weeping may endure for a night, joy will come in the morning!"

Just then, I heard the footsteps of the guards approaching, and the light from their torches began to illuminate my cell.

~

30

"AND HE SHALL REIGN FOREVER AND EVER!"

~

"Stand up, Isaiah!" the guards yelled. "Your appointed hour has come!"

They led me in shackles to the palace courtyard. Apparently, my execution would not take place in the darkness of the dungeon but rather out in the open for others to witness. Even though the sun was just beginning to rise, I could see the hatred etched on the faces of Manasseh's officials as they stood before me. They looked deranged as they shouted with one voice, "Death to the one who speaks falsely against his king!"

A wooden platform had been constructed overnight in the center of the courtyard with twelve rugged steps leading up to it. A large, roughly hewn wooden table had been placed in the center of the platform. Two men, who evidently were my executioners, stood on opposite sides of the table. Three guards led me onto the platform and told me to gaze up at one of the palace windows.

. . .

I saw Manasseh looking down at me with disgust and resentment. There was no question the one truly overseeing this moment was the evil one. Manasseh and the others had simply become pawns in his hands. The evil one feared the One whose coming I had foretold more than anything else, and he sought to silence my voice.

"My king," I shouted up to Manasseh, "it is still not too late for you to seek the Lord God Jehovah and turn from your evil ways. If you turn to Him in repentance, He will forgive you and heal your land. But if you do not, you will soon hear the marching feet of the Assyrian army as they come to take you captive. You will be bound as I am now and led away to a place you do not want to go."

The king's face remained unchanged as he stood there in silence. He simply signaled to the executioners to proceed. The guards removed my shackles, then tied my hands and my feet with ropes. They laid me on the table and bound my chest and legs to it so I could not move.

I saw the instrument to be used in my execution. It was a crosscut saw with handles on both ends. As I looked closer, I realized the saw had not been fashioned from metal but from wood. The executioners took their positions, one on each side of the table.

Apparently, the king had determined sawing my body in half with a dull wooden blade was the horrifying torture he sought. The dullness would prolong the agony.

I knew I would soon be in the presence of the Holy One of Israel. But this time, I would not enter His presence through a vision – this time I would be there in person. As I looked up, the heavens parted, and I saw the One whose coming I had foretold. He looked at me with compassion and assurance.

. . .

Surrounding Him was a multitude who formed a great cloud of witnesses. Some of the faces looked familiar, but others did not. However, I knew these men and women had one thing in common. They all looked forward by faith to the coming arrival of the Promised One – the One who promises He will never leave us nor forsake us.

As my executioners went about their task, I was no longer conscious of what they were doing. Rather, I was acutely aware of the beckoning of my Lord. He was more real to me now than anyone standing around me or anyone I had known on this earth. He stood with arms outstretched, welcoming me home into His kingdom. Everything around me would one day pass away, but His kingdom would endure forever.

And I heard those gathered around Him proclaiming His royal titles: "*Wonderful Counselor, Almighty God, Everlasting Father, Prince of Peace.*[1] Hallelujah! For the Lord God Omnipotent reigns … and He shall reign forever and ever!"

~

SCRIPTURE BIBLIOGRAPHY

~

Much of the story line of this book is taken from the books of 2 Kings, 2 Chronicles, and Isaiah. Certain fictional events or depictions of those events have been added.

Some of the dialogue in this story are direct quotations from Scripture. Here are the specific references for those quotations:

Chapter 1

(1) Amos 3:1-2

(2) Amos 3:6-7

(3) Amos 3:8

(4) Amos 2:4-5

Chapter 2

(1) 2 Chronicles 26:18

Chapter 4

[1] Isaiah 6:3

[2] Isaiah 6:3

Chapter 5

[1] Isaiah 6:5

[2] Isaiah 6:7

[3] Isaiah 6:8

[4] Isaiah 6:8

[5] Isaiah 6:9

[6] Isaiah 6:11

[7] Isaiah 6:11-13

Chapter 6

[1] Amos 7:7-9

[2] Amos 9:11-12

Chapter 8

[1] Deuteronomy 2:19

[2] 1 Samuel 11:11

Chapter 9

[1] Isaiah 5:1-6

[2] Isaiah 5:30

Chapter 10

[1] Isaiah 7:4, 7

[2] Isaiah 7:11

[3] Isaiah 7:12

[4] Isaiah 7:14

[5] Isaiah 7:17, 20

[6] Isaiah 7:21, 22, 25

[7] Isaiah 8:11-13, 22

Chapter 11

[1] 2 Chronicles 28:9-11

[2] 2 Chronicles 28:13

[3] 2 Kings 16:7

Chapter 13

[1] Isaiah 8:16; 9:1-2

[2] Isaiah 9:4, 6

[3] Isaiah 9:7

[4] Isaiah 10:4-5

[5] Isaiah 10:6-7

[6] Isaiah 10:12, 18-19

[7] Isaiah 10:20-22

[8] Isaiah 10:24-25, 34

[9] Isaiah 11:1, 6

Chapter 14

[1] 2 Chronicles 29:5-6

[2] 2 Chronicles 29:6, 8

[3] 2 Chronicles 29:10-11

[4] 2 Chronicles 30:6-9 (paraphrase)

Chapter 15

[1] Isaiah 14:29-31 (portions)

Chapter 16

(1) 2 Kings 18:14

(2) 2 Kings 18:14 (paraphrase)

Chapter 17

(1) 2 Chronicles 32:7-8

(2) 2 Kings 18:19-21

(3) 2 Kings 18:22; 2 Chronicles 32:13-14

(4) 2 Chronicles 32:15

(5) 2 Kings 18:23-25

(6) 2 Kings 18:31-32

(7) Isaiah 37:3-4

(8) Isaiah 37:6-7

Chapter 18

(1) Isaiah 37:23-29

(2) Isaiah 37:33-35

Chapter 19

(1) Isaiah 38:1

(2) Isaiah 38:3

Chapter 20

(1) 2 Kings 20:5-6

(2) 2 Kings 20:7

(3) 2 Kings 20:8

(4) 2 Kings 20:9

(5) 2 Kings 20:10

(6) Isaiah 38:16, 17, 20

Chapter 21

[1] Isaiah 39:3

[2] Isaiah 39:5-6

[3] Isaiah 39:7

[4] Isaiah 39:8

Chapter 22

[1] Isaiah 40:6

[2] Isaiah 40:6-7

[3] Isaiah 40:3-5

Chapter 24

[1] Isaiah 6:8

[2] Isaiah 49:4

[3] Isaiah 43:18-21

[4] Isaiah 49:5

[5] Isaiah 49:6

[6] Isaiah 49:7

[7] Isaiah 52:13-15

Chapter 25

[1] Isaiah 53:1

[2] Isaiah 53:2-3

[3] Isaiah 53:4-5

[4] Isaiah 53:6

[5] Isaiah 53:7-8

[6] Isaiah 53:8-10

[7] Isaiah 53:11-12

[8] Isaiah 54:2-4

[9] Isaiah 25:6-8

[10] Isaiah 25:8-10

Chapter 27

[1] 2 Chronicles 7:12, 15-16

[2] Isaiah 59:3

Chapter 28

[1] Isaiah 48:6-7

[2] Isaiah 48:8

[3] Isaiah 48:9-11

[4] Isaiah 48:12-13

[5] Isaiah 48:17-18

[6] Isaiah 48:19, 22

Chapter 29

[1] Isaiah 61:1

[2] Isaiah 61:2-3

Chapter 30

[1] Isaiah 9:6

LISTING OF CHARACTERS (ALPHABETICAL ORDER)

~

Many of the characters in this book are real people pulled directly from the pages of Scripture. i have not changed any details about those individuals except in some instances their interactions with the fictional characters. They are noted below as "UN" (unchanged).

In other instances, fictional details have been added to real people to provide additional background about their lives where Scripture is silent. The intent is to provide further information for the story. They are noted as "FB" (fictional background).

In some instances, we are never told the names of certain individuals in the Bible. In those instances, where i have given them a name as well as a fictional background, they are noted as "FN" (fictional name).

Lastly, a few of the characters are purely fictional, added to convey the fictional elements of these stories . They are noted as "FC" (fictional character).

~

Abijah – wife of Ahaz, daughter of King Zechariah of Israel (FB)
Abraham – the patriarch (UN)
Ahaz – 12th king of Judah, son of Jotham, father of Hezekiah, nephew of Isaiah (FB)
Ahio – wife of Jotham (FN)
Amaziah – 9th king of Judah, son of Joash, father of Uzziah, uncle of Isaiah (UN)
Amos – a prophet of God (FB)
Amoz – son of Joash, brother of Amaziah, father of Isaiah (UN)
Angel of the Lord - worshiping the Lord before His throne (UN)
Azariah – a high priest during King Uzziah's reign (UN)
Azrikam – commander of the palace of Judah under King Ahaz (UN)
David – king of Israel (before the kingdoms divided) (UN)
Elkanah – commander of the army of Judah under King Ahaz (UN)
Hanun – king of Ammon early 10th century BC, son of Nahash (UN)
Hephzibah – daughter of Isaiah and Nebiah, wife of Hezekiah, mother of Manasseh (FB)
Hezekiah – 13th king of Judah, son of Ahaz, father of Manasseh, son-in-law of Isaiah (FB)
Isaiah – a prophet of God, son of Amoz (FB)
Jecoliah – wife of Amaziah (UN)
Jehoaddan – wife of Joash (UN)
Jehoshaphat – 4th king of Judah, son of Asa, father of Jehoram (UN)
Jehovah God – the Sovereign and Almighty God (UN)
Jerushah – wife of Uzziah, mother of Jotham and Nebiah (FB)
Joash – 8th king of Judah, father of Amaziah and Amoz, grandfather of Isaiah (UN)
Jotham – 11th king of Judah, son of Uzziah, father of Ahaz, cousin and brother-in-law of Isaiah (FB)
Lot – nephew of Abraham (UN)
Maher-shalal-hash-baz – second son of Isaiah and Nebiah (FB)
Manasseh – 2nd son of Ahaz, sacrificed to pagan gods as a child (FC)
Manasseh – 14th king of Judah, son of Hezekiah (FB)
Meshullemeth – wife of Manasseh (FN)
Messiah, the Promised One – the Son of the Living God (UN)
Naamah – 1st daughter of Manasseh, great granddaughter of Isaiah (FC)
Nahash – king of Ammon mid 11th century BC (UN)
Nebiah – daughter of Uzziah, wife of Isaiah (FN)
Oded – a prophet of God (UN)

Pekah – 18th king of the northern kingdom of Israel (UN)
Rab-shakeh – Assyrian general under King Sennacherib (UN)
Rezin – king of Aram (UN)
Sennacherib – king of Assyria 705 – 681 BC (UN)
Shanip – king of Ammon mid 8th century BC (UN)
Shear-Jashub – oldest son of Isaiah and Nebiah (FB)
Solomon – king of Israel (before the kingdoms divided) (UN)
Tiglath – 3rd son of Ahaz (named in honor of Tiglath-Pileser), sacrificed to pagan gods as a child (FC)
Tiglath-Pileser III – king of Assyria 745 – 727BC (UN)
Unnamed daughter of Manasseh – 2nd daughter, sacrificed to pagan gods at birth (FC)
Uzziah – 10th king of Judah, son of Amaziah, father of Jotham, cousin of Isaiah (FB)

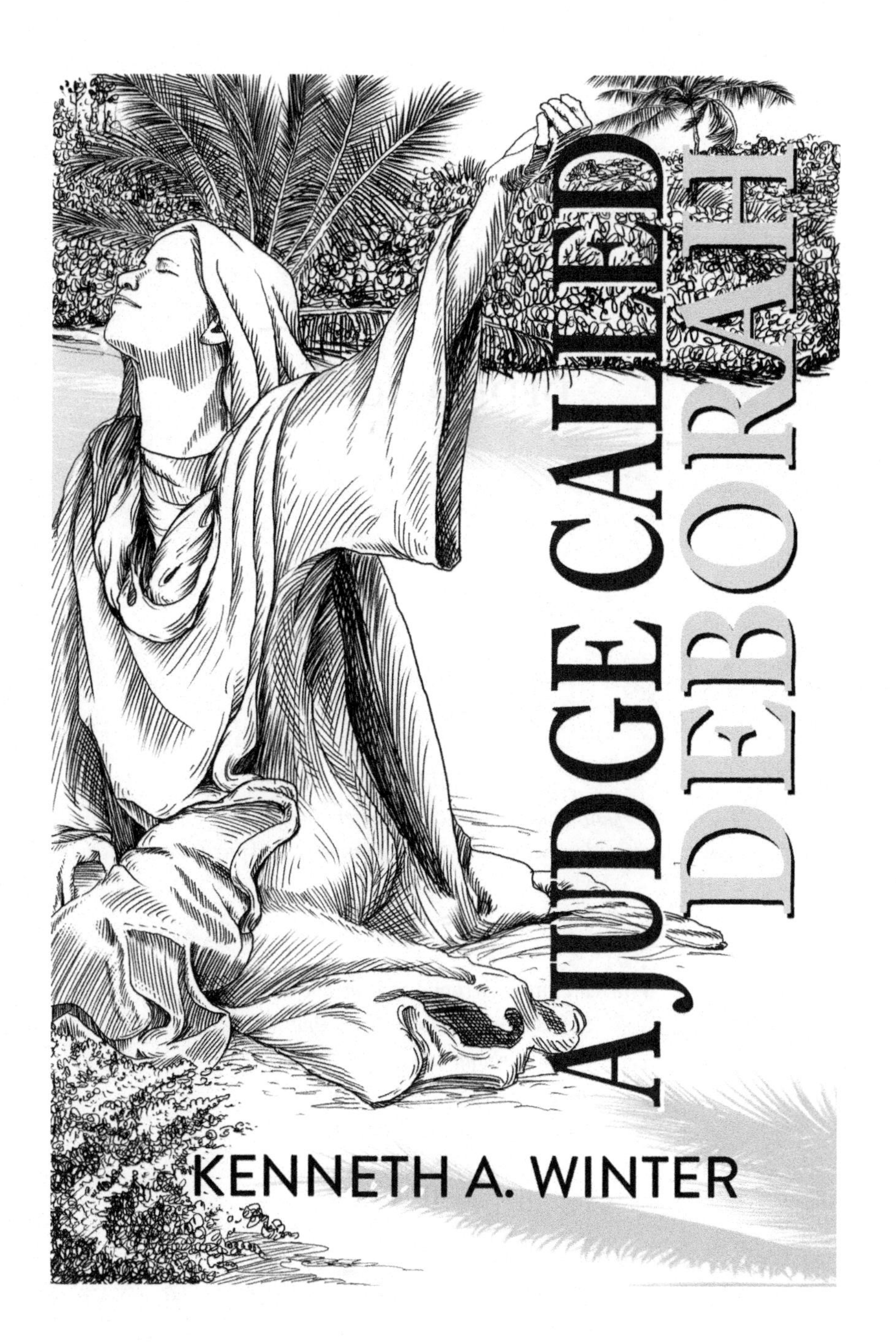
A JUDGE CALLED
DEBORAH
KENNETH A. WINTER

DEDICATION

To LaVonne,
for your constant prayers,
your enduring strength,
your abiding faith,
your unending encouragement, and
your steadfast love … for me … our family … and our Lord

~

Who can find a virtuous and capable wife?
She is more precious than rubies.
Her husband can trust her,
and she will greatly enrich his life.
She brings him good, not harm,
all the days of her life.
Proverbs 31:10-12

~

PREFACE

~

This fictional novella is the fourth book in a series titled, *The Called,* which is about ordinary people whom God called to use in extraordinary ways. We tend to elevate the people we read about in Scripture and place them on a pedestal far beyond our reach. We often think, "Of course God used them. They had extraordinary strength or extraordinary faith. But God could never use an ordinary person like me."

But nothing could be further from the truth. The reality is that throughout history God has used the ordinary to accomplish the extraordinary – and He has empowered them through His Holy Spirit.

In the days that followed the leadership of Moses and Joshua, the people of Israel repeatedly turned their backs on God and went their own way. Their sin inevitably led to their captivity by a foreign king who treated them cruelly. Each time, by His grace, God mercifully responded to His people's cries for help and raised up judges to lead them out of their captivity and back to Him. This is the story of one of those judges – an Ephraimite woman named Deborah.

Though she lived in a day when the culture dictated that women were to be seen and not heard, God raised up this woman of faith, wisdom, and courage to lead her people as a prophetess and the fourth judge over Israel. She courageously rallied her people to go up against one of the best-trained and best-equipped armies of the day because of her confidence in the Lord God Jehovah.

Though God chose her to be a leader for Israel, Deborah did not seek fame or recognition. Rather, she had the humility and wisdom to choose a respected warrior by the name of Barak to be the commander over the armies of Israel. God gave her the discernment to know He would raise up another woman named Jael to, in fact, become the champion of Israel in the ultimate defeat of their powerful enemy.

In these pages, i will endeavor to unfold the stories of each of these people so we can see how their lives were divinely linked for that moment in history. i do so to help us see them as real people God used through their unique circumstances in extraordinary ways.

i hope you will sit back and get to know each one as we walk through their lives. Most of the characters in the story come directly from Scripture. You will recognize them from the pages of the early chapters in the Book of Judges. In numerous instances, i have chosen to add background details about them that are not found in Scripture. i draw heavily on the historical writings of Josephus and the Jewish historical traditions passed down through rabbinical teachings. But please remember that some of the elements i have added are plausible fiction.

One fictional device i have used is Deborah's family tree as it unfolds through the story. Though many of the individuals introduced are real people, i have crafted fictional family relationships to introduce the era of the judges in Israelite history into the story. As in my other stories, i have also added fictional characters to round out the narrative. i have included a character map as an appendix in the back of the book to clarify the historical and fictional elements of each character.

Throughout the story, some instances of dialogue are direct quotes from Scripture – these will be italicized. The Scripture references are included in a bibliography in the back of the book. Dialogue not italicized is part of the fictional story that helps advance the narrative.

Finally, my prayer is that as you read this story, you will see Deborah through new eyes – and be challenged to live out your walk with the Lord with the same boldness, humility, and courage she displayed. And most importantly, i pray you will be challenged to be an "ordinary" follower with the willingness and faith to be used by God in extraordinary ways … for His glory!

~

1

JOSHUA IS DEAD

Joshua has been dead for many years. He was God's chosen leader over our people for the thirty years leading up to his death. God's anointing on him had been conspicuous. Moses had mentored him for the prior forty years to prepare him to step into his leadership role. The succession in leadership had been well-planned, and the transition between the two men had gone smoothly.

Joshua was a wise and effective leader. God clearly spoke to him, and he knew how to hear from God. He knew to seek God in all things. But it remains somewhat surprising that when he died there was no one who had been trained to take his place as leader over our people.

Yes, our people knew that Jehovah God was our Leader. We knew we were His people. But for seventy years He had guided our people through the voices of men. Surely, He intended to continue that pattern! So, where was the man He had chosen to follow in Joshua's footsteps? Had Joshua not been listening to God? Or, had Joshua been disobedient to God by not mentoring the next leader? Or, did God have a much different plan?

When God required a leader to lead His people out of Egypt through the wilderness to His Promised Land, He knew where to find him. He went to a hillside and selected the shepherd He had prepared for the task. Then when He required someone to lead the people into the Promised Land to possess the land, He chose a man who had proven his military leadership capability time and again.

In both instances, God's selection and anointing were obvious. He raised up leaders with the unique gifts and ability for the assignments He gave them. But those assignments were now completed. His people were now in possession of the land. God no longer required one leader to lead all the tribes. Now each individual tribe needed to conquer the territory God had selected for them. And God had raised up tribal leaders through Joshua's leadership.

It soon became obvious God had a new plan for the governing of Israel.

Soon after Joshua's death, the Canaanite tribes began to stir. They believed our people were vulnerable to an attack because of his death and the absence of a successor. But Jehovah God had a different strategy.

He spoke to the hearts of the tribal leaders, and they asked Him, *"Which tribe should go first to attack the Canaanites?"*(1)

The Lord answered, *"Judah, for I have given them victory over the land."*(2) The leaders exercised wisdom, heeded the word of the Lord, and advanced according to the Lord's plan instead of going out on their own.

The army of the tribe of Judah was under the command of Caleb. By then, he was the oldest person living among our people, with all the wisdom derived from his faithful walk with the Lord. And even at 110 years of age, he still had the strength and courage of a younger man to effectively lead the fighting men of Judah. Caleb knew God would give them all they needed to faithfully accomplish His task.

His first action was to lead the tribe of Judah, the largest tribe of Israel, to enlist the support and cooperation of the tribe of Simeon, the smallest tribe of Israel. The tribe of Simeon possessed an allotment of land within the borders of Judah – in essence, the hole inside of the wheel. And it was mutually beneficial for the tribes to collaborate to conquer the remaining Canaanites living within their borders.

The two tribes defeated the Canaanites in the hill country cities of Bezek, Jerusalem, and Hebron. As they approached the city of Debir, Caleb vowed to give his daughter Achsah in marriage to the man who successfully led in the attack and capture of the city. The champion proved to be Caleb's nephew, Othniel, who was an honorable man.

Shortly after Othniel and Achsah married, she urged her new husband to ask her father for a field. But she soon realized the land in the Negev her father gave Othniel contained no springs of water. She knew the land would need a good water source to be productive and bear fruit. Othniel hesitated to go back to his father-in-law with an additional request. So, Achsah boldly went to her father and asked:

"*Father, give me a further blessing,*" she said. "*You have been kind enough to give me land in the Negev, please give me springs as well.*"[3]

Caleb, obviously concerned about his daughter's welfare and happiness, gave them not one spring but two.

I tell you this story for several reasons. First, as a daughter of Israel, I am a descendant of that union between Othniel and Achsah. Their great-great-granddaughter was given in marriage to the Benjaminite Ehud, from whom I am also descended. Jehovah God has blessed me with a heritage of faithfulness, passed down from the men and women who have walked before me.

Second, God has taught me through them that He will always provide the gifts, abilities, and resources needed to accomplish His purpose. Just as He provided leaders like Moses, Joshua, and Caleb, He will provide just what is needed, when it is needed, for whatever time it is needed. He has taught me to expect His provision, trust His provision, and look to His provision – whatever or whoever it happens to be.

Third, He has shown me through them that even though He is the same today as He was yesterday, I should not expect Him to always do things the exact same way. He will do what is appropriate for the hour in the way that is needed. His plan to conquer the land was different from His plan to possess the land. And His plan for us to inhabit the land today will look different as well.

Lastly, God has shown me through my ancestors that we all have a part in God's plan. Just like Moses, Joshua, Caleb, Othniel, and Achsah, He has uniquely made each of us to be a part of His purpose. No one is excluded.

God instituted a new era of leadership over our people – the era of the judges. That story begins with Othniel and Achsah … and, in many ways, so does my story.

~

2

OTHNIEL AND ACHSAH

Not long after Othniel and Achsah settled in the city of Debir, Caleb was laid to rest. Our people's zeal to conquer the land in obedience to the Lord died with Caleb. Instead, they turned their attention to settling the land, and the many years of fighting became a fleeting memory. Until then, God had allowed them to enjoy the fruits of the labor of those who had ruled before them. But now, they busied themselves with the task of cultivating the fields and planting the crops.

The men and women who had been born in the wilderness and had no memory of our people's enslavement in Egypt, now had children who had no memory of the challenges of the wilderness or conquering the land. They became complacent.

Settling the land took on many meanings – not all of which were good. God had given our people very specific instructions through Moses and Joshua before we ever set foot in the Promised Land:

"As for the towns of the nations the Lord your God is giving you as a special possession, destroy every living thing in them. You must completely destroy the Hittites, Amorites, Canaanites, Perizzites, Hivites, and Jebusites, just as the Lord your God has commanded you. This will prevent the people of the land from teaching you to imitate their detestable customs in the worship of their gods, which would cause you to sin deeply against the Lord your God."(1)

But our people failed to do as God commanded. Rather than driving out the people who occupied the towns, they settled in their midst. Over time, many of our sons intermarried with their daughters and many of our daughters with their sons. Many of our people began to worship their gods and forgot about the Lord our God. In short, most of our people did evil in the eyes of the Lord and abandoned His ways.

But Othniel and Achsah continued to honor the Lord God Jehovah. As the years passed, He blessed them with two sons, Hathath and Meonothai. From an early age, each boy revealed his own unique penchant. God gave Hathath the ability to tend the earth. He was able to cultivate barren fields and transform them into rich and plentiful gardens and groves. Each year's harvest exceeded the previous one, and the other residents of Debir could not fail to see the hand of God's blessing upon him. Soon, the surrounding fields also showed an increase as each neighbor began to follow Hathath's instruction.

Meonothai, on the other hand, was a skillful hunter. God gifted him with the trained eye and instincts of his grandfather Caleb, who had served Pharoah well as the master of the hunt in the days of Egyptian slavery. Meonothai also demonstrated the courage of his father and the shrewdness of his mother. He, too, became a recognized leader among the people of Debir and the surrounding cities.

Othniel proceeded to lead his family and the other residents of Debir to honor the Lord God Jehovah in all things. In turn, God blessed his family and the city with peace and prosperity, even as most of Israel did what was evil in the sight of the Lord.

Twenty years had passed since Joshua led the Israelites in his last major military campaign – the defeat of the northern kings. King Jabin of Hazor had rallied the northern kings to join their forces against the Israelites. It was a combined force of 300,000 foot soldiers, together with 10,000 fighting men on horseback, and another 20,000 in iron chariots.

They were much better equipped than the fighting men Joshua led. From a human perspective, the odds against our people were overwhelming. But the northern kings had failed to take into consideration one critical factor. The kings knew what God had done in defeating the enemies of Israel, but still they had refused to turn to Him. It wouldn't have mattered if the fighting force had been ten times that number – the Lord God Jehovah would go before His people and defeat those who had denied His Name.

God caused confusion among their warriors, and they fled in retreat. The Israelites chased them for two days – killing the warriors, crippling the horses, and burning the chariots. Our people found King Jabin hiding in the city of Hazor and executed him as God directed.

The day before our people arrived in the city, King Jabin sent his ten-year-old son away to safety. He was taken to the northernmost part of the Aramean kingdom, to the area called Aram-Nahrayn. There the boy was raised with hatred in his heart toward the God of Israel and His people. That boy grew up to become King Cushan of Aram-Nahrayn. He had matured into adulthood with the singular focus of seeking vengeance against our people.

Though the fighting force of Aram-Nahrayn had been rebuilt to 50,000 men over the twenty years that had passed, Cushan's councilors continued to remind him of how his father's much greater force had been defeated. Their fear of defeat kept the young king in check … at least for a time.

However, the king and his advisors were not aware of the Lord God Jehovah's anger over the wickedness of His people. Most of the Israelites had abandoned Him to serve Baal and the images of Ashtoreth, and they had forsaken the one true God. So, though King Cushan's military was not as mighty as his father's, they would not be fighting against the Lord God Jehovah. He would be leading his men to fight against the men of Israel without the protection of their God. And Jehovah God had already determined the outcome. He would hand His people over to the Aramean king.

3

A NORTHERN KING IS UNLEASHED

The cities of the smaller northern tribes of Asher, Naphtali, Zebulun, and Issachar fell quickly to King Cushan's initial advance. Word of the attacks spread among the Israelites but was met with confusion and despair. Our people were no longer organized as a fighting force. They had no leader because they had forsaken the One to whom they should have turned.

Their easy victories emboldened Cushan and his councilors to plunge farther south into the cities occupied by our other tribes. Each city fell with little opposition. Our disobedience was quickly causing us to lose all that God had graciously given us. But still, our people continued to turn to their false gods.

Within a matter of months, Cushan had occupied all the land except what was inhabited by the tribes of Judah and Simeon. Though he was able to advance into the most northern cities of Judah, he was unsuccessful in his attacks on Debir or the cities surrounding it. Jehovah God had looked upon the faithfulness of Othniel and his family and had protected them.

Though Othniel, his sons, and the fighting men who joined them fought courageously and valiantly, they knew it was God who was truly keeping Cushan at bay.

Eventually King Cushan's advisors convinced him to be satisfied with his gains and not advance against the southern portion of Judah. They saw no reason to sustain further losses of their men. They reminded Cushan he had already conquered the cities of Ephraim, home to the descendants of Joshua, whom he blamed for the execution of his father, King Jabin.

So, Cushan turned his attention to the cities now under his control. He had no interest in making these cities part of his domain; rather, he planned to destroy them as retribution for what their fathers had done to his own father. He was determined to start with the cities of Ephraim. He began with Timnath-serah – the town Joshua had made his home.

Cushan's forces quickly identified Joshua's descendants – his grandsons and great-grandsons – and brought them before their king. He took great pleasure in torturing them before having them decapitated and their heads thrust onto long spikes positioned at the highest points of the town for all to see. Their wives and adult daughters were defiled and made to serve as slaves, while their children were taken away to Aram-Nahrayn to serve as slaves in the king's palace.

But that didn't quench Cushan's thirst for vengeance. He instructed his forces to torture and execute other tribal leaders in all the conquered towns and cities. The people throughout Israel were filled with fear and agony and began to refer to the king as Cushan-rishathaim – "the doubly wicked" Cushan. No one could remember another leader having been so evil. Truth be told, even the Arameans began to fear their king's lust for blood.

As the years passed, the Israelites continued in their spiritual blindness and cried out to their false gods for help – but none ever came. Finally, they remembered the God of their fathers – the Lord God Jehovah – and called out to Him for deliverance.

Throughout those same years, Othniel, his sons, and neighbors continued to hear reports of the havoc being wreaked upon the cities to the north. Although they had been successful in repulsing Cushan at their own gates, they feared their military would be insufficient to rescue their northern neighbors. As a result, they remained paralyzed by their fear and did nothing.

It was Achsah who called on Jehovah God throughout those years seeking His direction on what the people of Judah should do. The land of Israel had suffered at the hands of King Cushan for eight years when God finally spoke to Caleb's daughter.

She immediately went to her husband just as God had directed her and said, "Othniel, the Lord God Jehovah has said you are to go forth in His Spirit and lead His people out of their bondage. Just as He was with Moses, Joshua, and my father, He will be with you. He will go before you, and just as Joshua led our people to defeat King Jabin, you will lead our people to defeat his son, King Cushan."

Emboldened and empowered by the Spirit of God, Othniel sent out word to all the free cities of Judah and Simeon. "Brothers, the God of our fathers has promised He will deliver our brothers and sisters who are in bondage to the Arameans. We are to assemble and march on their cities and defeat their captors. Do not fear King Cushan-rishathaim because the Lord our God will go before us as our banner and our shield."

Over the next several days, the men assembled on the plain to the north of Debir to become a fighting force of 80,000 men. They did not have the weaponry, chariots, or cavalry of the Arameans – but they had something far more powerful. They had the Spirit of God going before them!

Throughout the years, Cushan and his forces had become complacent. They believed their reign of terror over the Israelites had made them incapable of rebellion. So, they were not expecting an attack when the army of Judah and Simeon appeared at the gates of Jerusalem. The Aramean response was too little too late, and within moments the Israelites living in the city had been freed of their eight-year captivity.

From there, Othniel led the fighting men from city to city. Though the Arameans were now prepared for attack, their efforts made little difference. The God of Israel was always victorious, and His army marched with praises to Him on their lips. More men joined the fighting force from each city as they were freed, and soon their number exceeded a quarter of a million fighting men.

4

THE FIRST JUDGE IS RAISED UP OVER ISRAEL

~

Othniel's spies reported that King Cushan was assembling most of his fighting force around the city of Timnath-serah. He was determined to stand his ground there at the homeplace of Joshua. Othniel knew Cushan's forces had the advantage of higher ground, but he also knew he had the greater advantage – Jehovah God was going before His people.

The night before the planned attack, the Lord gave Othniel this promise: "Do not be afraid of King Cushan. By this time tomorrow, he and his army will be dead men. Then you must cripple their horses and burn any chariots that remain."

The Lord told Othniel he and his fighting men should not form ranks in Timnath-serah as Cushan would expect. Rather, they should follow the same instructions the Lord God gave Joshua when he defeated King Jabin. They were to immediately attack the enemy.

Othniel followed the Lord's instructions, and Cushan and his men were caught by surprise. Israel's fighting men were already upon them before they could mobilize their cavalry or their chariots to attack. Cushan and his commanders became so confused and disoriented their warriors began to flee.

However, Cushan refused to retreat. He went to the highest vantage point and shouted at his men to stand their ground and fight – but to no avail. The battle was lost, and his men bolted in droves. Our men pursued them and followed the Lord's instruction not to leave any man alive.

Unlike his father who hid in defeat, Cushan was enraged and shouted taunts at Othniel. "Let this battle be decided by the fate of the two of us!" he screamed. Both men knew Cushan was the younger of the two and had the physical advantage. But Othniel knew his trust was not in his own power but in the Spirit of the Lord.

The two warriors met at the gates of the city with swords in hand. Their one-on-one battle continued for more than an hour, and both men were physically spent. Cushan's strength came from his hatred; Othniel's from the Spirit of the Lord. Both men lost their footing several times during the match, but each time they were able to regain their position – until finally Othniel struck the blow that brought Cushan to his knees.

As Othniel looked into Cushan's eyes, all he saw was defiance. Cushan did not plead for mercy for himself or his men. There was no regret for his actions. He seethed with hatred directed not only at Othniel but more vehemently toward Jehovah God. His rage stamped such an indelible expression on his face that it remained even after Othniel's true blade severed Cushan's head from his body. As his body collapsed to the ground, the attempted retreat of the remaining Arameans who had continued to fight beside Cushan was immediately foiled.

Not only were the people of Timnath-serah set free that day, but so were all of the remaining people of Israel who lived in the other cities that had been conquered by the Arameans. There was little left of the Arameans once the fighting was done. They would not rise again to attempt vengeance upon God's people. News traveled quickly throughout the surrounding lands that the God of Israel had once again rescued His people and defeated His enemy.

Once the fighting was over, Othniel and his sons returned to their home in Debir. Jehovah God established Othniel as a judge over all of Israel to institute justice and the practice of His law among all the people. There was peace in the land for the next forty years.

One year before he was laid to rest with his ancestors, Othniel witnessed the birth of his great-great granddaughter, Ayala, through the line of his son, Meonothai. Eighteen years later, she would be given in marriage to a Benjamite living in the village of Ai. His name was Ehud, and he was the man God would raise up to be the second judge of Israel.

In the years following Othniel's death, the people of Israel again turned their hearts away from the Lord and did evil in His sight. During those years, a cunning king of Moab ascended to his throne and began to put a plan in place to conquer Israel. He craftily entered an alliance with the Amalekites, who inhabited the lands on the south side of the tribes of Israel, and the Ammonites, who inhabited those on the east side. Once that alliance was in place, the Lord permitted the Moabite king to take control over His rebellious people.

Unlike Cushan, King Eglon of Moab was not motivated by vengeance against Israel in retribution for past injuries; rather, for him it began over a territorial dispute. You will recall that the tribes of Reuben and Gad, together with half of the tribe of Manasseh, were allowed by God to settle on the east side of the Jordan River. You will also recall that it was God's intention that all His people settle in the Promised Land, but He had permitted their request to settle for less than His best.

A portion of the land given to the tribe of Gad by Moses had been seized when the Israelites defeated the Amorites. But the Moabites had always believed that portion of land belonged to them – and not the Amorites – and even less, the tribe of Gad.

For almost one hundred years the people of Moab had resented the confiscation of what they believed to be their land – until one day King Eglon resolved to do something about it.

5

A REBELLIOUS PEOPLE AND A DEFIANT KING

~

Jericho was the first city Jehovah God led our people to defeat when they entered the Promised Land. After He led the people to destroy the city, He invoked this curse:

"May the curse of the Lord fall on anyone who tries to rebuild the city of Jericho. At the cost of his firstborn son, he will lay its foundation. At the cost of his youngest son, he will set up its gates."[1]

The city remained in ruins from that day forward, even though our people eventually forgot the curse and, even worse, turned their backs on the God who had pronounced it. After conquering the cities of Israel, King Eglon decided to establish a summer palace in the region to reinforce his rule over the land. His palace would be built on top of the ruins of Jericho, placing his own mark and majesty over the land.

He chose Jericho for two reasons. First, the city was strategically located as a gateway between the lands of Moab, Amon, and Israel. But the second reason was of even greater importance to Eglon. When he learned why the Israelites had not rebuilt the city, his decision to do so was intended to communicate his defiance of the God of Israel.

The Moabite king used Israelite slave labor to construct the palace; it took eight years to complete. When it was finished, the colonnaded structure eclipsed every other building in the region, and its comforts surpassed even those of Eglon's palace in Moab.

Unbeknownst to Eglon, God had seen his defiance and was already at work to bring about the destruction of that palace and the one who dared to place his throne within it. God's plan of destruction would include a Benjaminite by the name of Ehud.

While Othniel was still judge over Israel, he instituted a leadership structure whereby each tribe of Israel selected a judge. Othniel, in turn, delegated responsibility to each of the tribal judges to oversee the system of justice and practice of the law. Ehud's grandfather had served as the first tribal judge of Benjamin under Othniel.

When Othniel died, the tribes could not agree on a way to select one judge to preside over them all. Regrettably, none of them sought Jehovah God for His direction. Instead, they chose not to select one judge over them all. Each tribe, however, did continue the practice of being governed by its respective tribal judge. The mantle of that leadership passed from one generation to the next. When Ehud's grandfather died, Ehud's father, Gera, became the judge of Benjamin.

Gera, like the other judges who ruled when Eglon conquered the people, had turned away from God. The judges were now self-seeking, ineffective leaders who were the means by which King Eglon could impose his will. He tasked them with the gathering of an annual financial tribute from their respective tribes and presenting it to him. Once his summer palace was completed, he directed them to bring it to him there.

When Gera died, the mantle of leadership for the tribe of Benjamin passed to Ehud. Like his father, his heart had turned away from Jehovah God. However, the Lord led Ehud to marry Ayala, a righteous young woman who had never turned her heart away from the God of Israel. She had continued to seek Him with all her heart, just like her fathers before her.

Ayala continued to bear witness to her husband: "The same God who led our people out of the bondage of Egypt and delivered us from the wickedness of King Cushan is able to again deliver His people from the hands of King Eglon. All He seeks is for us to turn from our wicked ways and turn our hearts back to Him. He promises that if we seek Him, we will find Him. If we turn to Him with our whole hearts, He will turn His face toward us.

"Husband, our people will look to their leaders. If you don't repent and turn to Him, how will they ever do so?"

Before long, Ehud heeded those words and turned his heart to Jehovah God. The people of Benjamin began to see the change in his actions and his words. He tore down the altars he had erected to false gods and instead openly worshiped the Lord. Soon people began to follow his example and called out to God for forgiveness and deliverance. Word spread to the other tribes, and soon they, too, began to cry out to the Lord for help.

The time came when the annual tribute from the people was due to be delivered to King Eglon. Ehud and the other tribal judges came together to fast, pray, and seek the Lord in what He would have them do.

After three days, Ehud spoke to the other judges. "I believe the Lord has shown me we are to gather the tribute and deliver it to him as usual. We are to trust God that He will show us what we are to do after that."

By faith, the people of Israel did as Ehud had said. And Ehud did one other thing the Lord had shown him. He crafted a double-edged dagger that was eighteen inches long and placed it in a sheath strapped to his right thigh under his clothing.

~

6

A TRIBUTE THAT LED TO FREEDOM

~

Ehud was left-handed. The men and women of Ai had repeatedly reminded his parents when he was young, he wouldn't amount to much because of this trait. His father and mother had tried to retrain him to use his right hand, but they were unsuccessful. Despite this perceived handicap, he had grown into a very capable and accomplished young man.

Though no one had ever heard of a left-handed tribal judge, when the time came for him to assume the role for the tribe of Benjamin, there was no doubt he was the man for the task. Little did they know Jehovah God had uniquely equipped him for the task he would be called upon to carry out.

Each year, King Eglon demanded the Israelite tribes present a tribute greater than the year before. This year he had demanded twelve tons of silver (one from each tribe) and one ton of gold from the tribes combined. Twenty-eight ox-drawn carts were required to transport it. Ehud, together with the other tribal judges, set out on their journey to deliver the annual tax payment to Jericho.

Though much of Jericho was still in ruins, King Eglon's magnificent palace was located at the highest point of the city on a man-made plateau. It was no easy venture to lead the heavily laden ox carts to that point in the city. As Ehud and the others approached the palace, they passed the Moabite idols lining the pathway. As they arrived, they could see the king sitting on his throne in the center of a colonnaded portico that extended from the main building. It provided the setting for visitors and subjects to approach the king with great pomp and ceremony.

The ornate jeweled throne on which Eglon sat was twice the width of what one would expect. It had been crafted to accommodate the king's great girth. He was so fat his neck blended into his shoulders and his head appeared to straddle his body like a pebble on a boulder. It would have been comical if the king's actions and behavior had not been so repulsive.

He was surrounded by a multitude who seemed to comprise his royal court. Tables laden with great mounds of food of all kinds were stationed on every side. Ehud could not help but think of the people of Israel who were starving while this king gorged himself.

King Eglon's voice was shrill as he directed the men to unload the tribute into his treasury under the watchful eye of the palace guards. After our men completed their task, they were told they could leave. The journey down took much less time, and once the other judges and ox carts had departed the city, Ehud turned back toward the palace.

As he arrived at the portico, the guards advanced to protect their king. Ehud called out to Eglon, "*I have a secret message for you.*"(1)

"What could an Israelite have to say to me that would be of any importance?" the king mockingly replied.

"I have a message for you from the God of Israel," Ehud declared.[2]

The crowd surrounding Eglon began to laugh and ridicule Ehud. But he stood his ground staring intently at the Moabite king. Eglon looked back at him, and slowly the smirk disappeared from his face.

The king rose to his feet with the assistance of two servants. "I will speak with this man in my royal chamber," he commanded. Guards accompanied their king as he made his way to his chamber then looked uncertain as to whether they should remain. As they helped him settle onto his throne, he waved his hand directing them to leave. After a few minutes, only Ehud and King Eglon remained in the room.

"What is this message you have for me from the God of Israel?" he demanded of the Israelite. As he asked the question, he attempted to again rise to his feet.

At that moment, Ehud reached with his left hand, pulled out the dagger strapped to his right thigh, and thrust it into the king's belly. The dagger went so deep that the handle disappeared beneath the king's fat. Ehud made no attempt to withdraw the blade. The king slumped back onto his throne, and his bowels emptied though the open wound. Eglon made no sound. His body shuddered … and then he died.

Ehud carefully closed and locked the doors leading into the royal chamber before making his way to the latrine and escaping through the sewage access. When the servants returned to check on their king, they found the doors to the chamber locked. The odor that assaulted their noses led them to believe the king was relieving himself, so they respectfully waited.

After a long delay, when the king had still not come out, they became concerned and got the key to unlock the doors. They discovered their king slumped dead on his throne. A cry immediately went out to find the Israelite. "He has murdered the king!" they shouted.

Ehud, however, had escaped the palace as the servants were waiting outside the chamber. He was now making his way speedily on the horse that had been left waiting for him. The other judges were already sounding a call to arms as they made their way back to their respective tribes. Ehud went directly to Ai, alerting the people of his village.

"Follow me!" he cried. *"The Lord has given you victory over Moab your enemy!"*(3)

The Israelites took control of the lands surrounding Jericho and the shallows of the Jordan River, preventing the Moabites from advancing. Ten thousand of the strongest and bravest Moabite warriors died. Not one escaped!

So it was that Israel was freed from Moabite captivity that day, and Ehud became the second judge over all of Israel.

7

AN OX GOAD

~

The land was at peace for eighty years, and then Ehud was laid to rest.

But the day soon returned when our people forgot the oppression of the Moabites and embraced evil once again as they worshiped false gods. Some even turned into thieves and bandits, menacing the roads, and making travel unsafe.

Without any regard for a righteous God, lawlessness reigned over the land. Brother turned against brother. Selfishness and covetousness became standards of the day. In many respects, I think it would have been better if the threat had come from foreign people – at least that would have given us a common enemy. Instead, we became our own enemy. Marauding bands sprang up from within our own tribes.

Due to distrust, villages became isolated from one another. We were no longer one people; we weren't even twelve tribes. We had become a people divided into hundreds of clans, all suspicious of one another. It didn't take long for our outside enemies to discover our vulnerability. The first to attack were the Philistines who occupied the land to the northwest of Judah.

Ehud's grandson, Anath, was now the judge of the people in the village of Ai. He continued to walk in the ways of his grandfather, as did most of those living in the village. Even though it was difficult to see the Spirit of God at work in most of Israel, Ai was an exception. Jehovah God continued to bless this village. Ai's people enjoyed plentiful harvests and the favor of God in everything they did. In some ways, Ai became a light on a hill in the midst of a very dark land.

Anath did not take those blessings for granted. He knew they were the result of God's faithfulness to them more than it was their faithfulness to Him. A story had passed from generation to generation about how our patriarch Abraham had built an altar to worship the Lord in the hill country between Bethel and Ai. Over 500 years earlier, God had promised Abraham He would give this land to Abraham's offspring – and our people were now enjoying the fruit of that promise.

Ehud had begun the practice of going to that place in the shadow of the oak trees each year and offering a sacrifice of thanksgiving to God. Anath had continued the practice, and the annual time was now approaching. Though Anath knew those hills were no longer a safe place to travel, he also knew he needed to continue to do so and trust God for protection.

When the day arrived, he and his oldest son, Shamgar, set out on the half-day's journey to the altar with an ox that would be offered as the sacrifice. Shamgar had become an accomplished herdsman and used his long pointed ox goad to drive the animal in the path before them.

The men arrived at the place at midday without incident. Together they repointed the stones of the altar, gathered wood, and made the needed preparations. Then they lit the fire and offered the sacrifice as a thanksgiving offering to Jehovah God.

As they were preparing to leave, first one arrow and then another passed within inches of their heads and struck a nearby tree. The two men immediately ducked for cover as more arrows quickly followed. Anath and Shamgar counted ten attackers and, based on their appearance, decided the men were a Philistine war party. The father and son were clearly at a disadvantage – all they had were their hunting knives, one bow, a few arrows, and Shamgar's ox goad.

Suddenly the Philistines charged them. Anath knew they were too close to use his bow and arrows, so he picked up a piece of wood to use as a club, and Shamgar reached for his goad. The two men fought valiantly. When the clash was over, all of the Philistines were dead. As Shamgar looked around for his father, he saw him lying on the ground with a fatal wound to the side of his head.

Shamgar's anguish was quickly replaced by overwhelming anger. He wanted vengeance and justice for what the Philistines had done. But first, he needed to take his father's body back to Ai for proper burial. He fabricated a stretcher and set out on the journey. It was almost nighttime when he finally arrived back at the village. His family and friends immediately set about burying Anath's body as the law of Moses required.

Shamgar mourned for seven days before he set out on his mission of revenge. During the weeks that followed, he showed no mercy as he killed 600 Philistines with his ox goad. Fear of him spread throughout Philistia and no other war parties assaulted Israel. Shamgar's mother finally convinced him to stop pursuing the Philistines. He did so in honor of her. But until the day he died, there wasn't a man in Philistia – or Israel – who didn't fear him. Ai became a very safe place to live.

I would like to say the people of Israel turned back to God under the leadership of a judge named Shamgar. But the simple truth is, they did not. Our people continued to do evil in the sight of the Lord … and nothing my grandfather, Shamgar, had done made any difference.

8

A BEE

~

From the time I was a young girl, I remember my father telling me stories of my ancestors – Caleb, Othniel, Ehud, and Shamgar. He told me how God had used these men to lead our people in the way they should go. My father taught me about their courage. And most importantly, he taught me about their faith in Jehovah God.

But truth be told, my mother's stories influenced me even more. She recounted the lesser-known accomplishments of Achsah and Ayala. She told me about the strength and courage Achsah learned from her father to always do right even when others do not. She taught me to have the boldness of Achsah and never be afraid to ask God to provide all He has promised. She explained how Achsah had been the one to convince her husband to lead the men of Judah against King Cushan.

She also explained how the Spirit of God had worked through Ayala to lead her husband to repent of his sinful ways and turn his heart to Jehovah God. God had used her to provoke the courage in Ehud to lead our people to defeat the Moabites.

And my mother taught me how God had used my great-grandmother to calm my grandfather's heart and bring peace to our village of Ai. God had used each of these women to ultimately lead our people to follow God.

"That's why your father and I named you Deborah," my mother told me. "As you know, we also use that word to describe the insect that some refer to as a 'bee.' In the Oral Torah, our people are often compared to a 'deborah' (or a bee). Just as the nature of the bee is to collect pollen and nectar for others, so it is that we toil as a people – not for our own benefit, but for the purpose of bringing pleasure to our Father in heaven.

"Just as a bee's sting is used to inflict pain on those who do not go in the right way, the honey it produces is used to bring sweetness to the lives of those who do.

"And just as bees swarm behind a queen bee, so too do our people follow behind those who teach them and guide them in the Lord's wisdom and strength.

"Your father and I have prayed since before you were born that you might be a deborah that God uses, as He did your ancestors, to guide our people in wisdom and in strength. But do not lose sight that a deborah is a lowly insect. Allow your name to remind you to always remain humble no matter how God might work through you in the days ahead!"

Though the people of Ai continued to follow the Lord, most of the surrounding villages had long since turned away from Him. When my grandfather was still alive, our neighbors knew not to provoke the people of our village – they remembered vividly what had happened to the Philistines. Even the surrounding nations remained at bay. But when word spread that my grandfather had died, everything slowly began to change.

My father, Oded, followed in his father's footsteps and led our village in the ways of the patriarchs. He led the people to defend against attacks and assaults from our surrounding neighbors, but he was not the feared fighter his father had been. He was actually a gentle man with a quiet spirit.

When I came of age, my parents gave their blessing for me to marry an Ephraimite man named Lappidoth. We had known one another since childhood, and our union had been expected for many years. Lappidoth was a kind and tender man, much like my father, and I knew it was God's will for me to become his wife. But Lappidoth and I both knew I would never be a demure wife who remained quietly in the shadows!

Over the years, the Spirit of God has spoken words of wisdom and truth through me. As I grew older, my father – at first secretly – began to seek my counsel on matters people brought before him as the judge of our village. But as time passed, he began to openly seek my wisdom. In fact, the villagers soon realized he was coming to me, and some began to appeal to me directly.

When the time came that my father could no longer serve as leader of the village, he was unclear on what to do. Since I was an only child, he had no son to step up and take his place. He initially considered naming Lappidoth as his successor. But the more he considered the choice, the more uncertain he became. One day he came to me and asked my opinion.

"Deborah, it will soon be time for me to relinquish my role as judge over this village and name my successor," he said. "I had hoped your husband might be prepared to step into that position, but I now know he is less capable than I have been. I prayed that God would raise up sons through your union who could one day do so, but He has chosen to favor you with daughters.

"Daughter, what do you believe the Lord would have me do?"

As I pondered his question, I already knew the answer. But I sensed the Spirit of the Lord telling me to remain silent on the issue. Instead, He led me to say, "Father, you must continue to ask Jehovah God to show you the one He has chosen to be the next judge over our village. He will make it clear to you. Be careful to listen for His answer … and when He does, you will know what to do."

9

A CANAANITE KING AND A SARDINIAN MERCENARY

Over 250 years had passed since God had used Joshua and Caleb to lead our people to conquer and destroy the northern kingdoms of Canaan. The city of Hazor had been captured and burned to the ground; its king, Jabin, had been killed. Every living thing in the city was destroyed – except for the king's son who was secretly extracted from the city just days earlier.

Twenty years later, that son, King Cushan, followed in his father's footsteps and was killed at the hands of Othniel. Again, God gave our people victory and the cities under the king's rule were destroyed. But his lineage lived on in the village of Harosheth-Goiim.

For over two hundred years the descendants of Jabin and Cushan awaited the day they would exact their revenge on the people of Israel. When Shamgar was judge over Ai, an heir to the throne of Jabin named Tirshi rose to rule over his people. He led them to return to the site of Hazor and rebuild it. Since most of our people were doing what was right in their own eyes, he met no opposition. Soon the rebuilt city was prospering, and the number of its inhabitants was increasing daily.

King Tirshi saw the division among our people and knew the day of retribution against us was drawing near. He was so certain that he even named his newborn son Jabin. The conquered would rise to become the conqueror. And if it didn't occur during Tirshi's rule, he was certain young Jabin would lead his people to victory over Israel.

But Jabin grew to be a man of slight stature and frame. He would not be the warrior on the battlefield that Cushan had been. Neither did he appear to have his patronym's cunning or ability to lead his people in such an undertaking without significant help.

Tirshi's plan took a turn when his physicians diagnosed him with a terminal illness. The king knew his son needed to be surrounded by trusted advisors if the Hazorite kingdom was to rule the region once again.

Tirshi asked his generals to find a suitable military leader for his son. The one they selected was a general named Sisera. He figuratively and literally stood head and shoulders above the rest – despite the fact he was an outsider.

Years earlier, a young man arrived in Hazor from the island of Sardinia seeking fame and fortune. His fighting skills and courage enabled him to succeed as a mercenary. He didn't much care who hired him if they paid the bounty he demanded. Tirshi's thirst for vengeance against the Israelites provided a showcase for Sisera to display his talents. Soon, he was training others how to fight. In short, the Hazorites needed a leader who wasn't afraid to fight, and Sisera needed a fight for which he would be well paid. It was a mutually beneficial alliance.

As time went by, Sisera rose in the ranks of the Hazorite army. When Tirshi needed a trusted general to come alongside his son and command the army, Sisera was the obvious choice. Sisera would be loyal to Jabin – as long as Jabin paid him handsomely.

Tirshi had fueled a hatred in his son's heart for our people since Jabin was a little boy. By the time Tirshi died, King Jabin had no doubt that his destiny was to lead his people to destroy their Israelite enemies.

Jabin placed all his resources at Sisera's disposal to build an unbeatable fighting force. Iron was mined and fabricated to manufacture 900 chariots. Sisera convinced Jabin he needed to import Giara horses, native to the island of Sardinia. Sisera contended their size and strength were best suited for the soldiers' needs so Jabin authorized the purchase of 2,000 horses.

Sisera continued to build and equip his fighting force. Though it would be smaller than the army defeated by Joshua, it would be better prepared. Sisera was convinced his well-trained and well-equipped force would easily conquer our divided people.

Unbeknownst to Sisera, his greatest advantage was that our God would not be going before us; rather, the Lord was prepared to turn us over to Jabin and Sisera. Our people's evil actions and attitudes were a stench in the nostrils of Jehovah God. Not only would He not protect us, but He would permit the Hazorite army to be the hand of retribution He would use to discipline us.

~

10

A NEW JUDGE IN AI

~

While my father was still the judge of Ai, Jabin sent out his forces under the command of Sisera to conquer the northern city of Dan. The Danites were ill-prepared for the assault, and the city came under the control of Sisera within hours. Soon the sacrifice altars to Jehovah God were pulled down and replaced by ones to Canaanite idols. Our people were even less capable of withstanding the religious invasion than they had been to defend against the military attack.

One by one the other northern cities fell to Sisera's forces at an accelerated pace. The early military victories emboldened Jabin's resolve to unleash his vengeance on all our cities. It was early in Sisera's campaign that my father came to me seeking advice on who should follow him as judge.

A few days after our initial conversation, my father returned to me. "Deborah, last night Jehovah God spoke to me through a dream," he announced. "I dreamt that the walls of the city were encircled by Sisera and his army. Our people were fighting against his advance, but it was obvious our gate would soon be overrun.

"I called out to my mighty men who surrounded me saying, 'Is there no one who will meet Sisera at the gate and defeat him?' I looked at one man after another, but each of them turned away from me. Until one person walked into our midst and declared, 'I will go! With God's strength, I will defeat Sisera and his army. Allow me to go!'

"Deborah, that person was you! You were dressed in the armor of a warrior, but you spoke with the resolve of a judge! And at that moment, I knew God was raising you up to be our champion. God was telling me you are to be the next judge over Ai! And if He has chosen you, who am I to say otherwise? The one I have been seeking has been standing right before me all the time!"

My father paused and waited for me to reply. There was no doubt in my heart or mind that God had been preparing me for this day. But even though I knew my father welcomed my counsel, I also knew he had never considered me as his replacement until that moment. And I also knew few people in our city would look favorably on a female judge. But I knew with that same certainty God had chosen me for this role, and He would make the way for me to step into the position.

My father called our people together. They were not surprised He was preparing to name his successor since everyone knew he had been searching for weeks. But they were shocked when he announced it was me. A woman had never been a judge in Ai – and to the best of everyone's recollection, there had never been a female judge in all of Israel.

My father explained how God had confirmed to him that I was His choice for the role. Then he began to remind them of ways they had already seen me demonstrate the ability to serve in that capacity.

He called to one of the men standing in front of him. "Elias, do you remember when you and Reuben came before me seeking judgment on your property dispute? Do you remember it was Deborah who spoke up and helped the two of you settle your differences? Did she not demonstrate her wisdom as a judge that day?

"And Jacob, when Asa's ox injured you, who was it that ultimately settled the argument between the two of you?"

"It was Deborah," Jacob hesitantly replied.

My father continued to ask similar questions to other men standing around him. Each time the men acknowledged how God had used me to help them settle their conflicts.

"I turned to Deborah in each of those matters," my father continued, "because I knew God had given her the needed wisdom. And each of you came to know that as well. Why would you now not welcome her to serve as your new judge?"

For a few minutes, the men and women surrounding my father looked down in silence. Finally, one man and then another raised their heads and said, "When the time comes, may God grant Deborah the wisdom to judge over us."

That time came sooner than I expected. Several weeks later, my father fell ill with a fever. Nothing seemed to help, and his condition worsened. One afternoon, he mustered all his strength and called me to kneel by his bedside. He reached out and placed his frail hand upon my head.

As he began to pray, his voice suddenly got stronger: "Hear me, Oh Lord God of Israel! You have blessed me above all men with a loving wife, a beautiful daughter, and dear family and friends. You have blessed me with this daughter, whom You have anointed with great wisdom. You have chosen her to follow me as the judge of Ai.

"Grant her the wisdom and courage to accomplish all that You set before her in the days ahead. Grant her husband, children, and the people of this city the ability to support her in the responsibility You have given her. Grant her the bravery she will need to turn back the enemy that advances on Your people. And grant her Your favor in defeating that enemy – not only that Ai is protected from siege but also that there is peace throughout Israel.

"Grant her the strength to rise up like the sun, and grant that her name is recorded in the history of our people as one of our great leaders – following in the footsteps of Joshua, Caleb, Othniel, and Ehud. And cause our people to follow her steadfastly as she leads them to follow You."

As he finished his prayer, my father took his last breath … with his hand still resting on my head.

~

11

A FATHER'S BETRAYAL

~

When my ancestors, Caleb and Othniel, defeated the Canaanites to conquer the cities in the hill country, they were assisted by the Kenites, descendants of Moses's brother-in-law, Hobab. When the fighting was over, the Kenites settled among the Amalekites near the town of Arad.

Over the years, the alliance between our people and theirs remained strong. Each time our people rose up against our oppressors under the leadership of Othniel, Ehud, and Shamgar, the Kenites stood with us shoulder to shoulder in battle. But in more recent days, the Kenites turned away from the God of Moses and Hobab. They worshiped the gods of the Amalekites, which caused the relationship between our two peoples to become one of military convenience and not one of kinship and shared faith.

When King Tirshi was rebuilding the Hazorite kingdom with an eye on conquering Israel, part of his plan was to build alliances with the clans living among us – including the Kenites. He reminded the clans that this land had once been their home while our people were still slaves in Egypt. He rekindled a resentment against our people and encouraged the clans' support in helping him return the land to its rightful owners.

In truth, Tirshi had no intention of returning the land to its original owners. But the clans naively embraced his deception. Abdon, the clan leader of the Kenites, chose to join him as an ally. Abdon and Tirshi soon developed what appeared to be a friendship. Upon Tirshi's death, Jabin was quick to solidify that relationship between Abdon and himself.

When Jabin began to conquer the cities of Judah, he shrewdly left the town of Arad in the hands of the Kenites. Jabin and Sisera arrived at Arad's gates with great pomp and pageantry bearing spoils from their victories as gifts for Abdon. The Kenites welcomed them into the city as victorious allies. Abdon arranged for a feast in their honor that would last for seven days.

Abdon's eight sons were skilled hunters, and he instructed them to keep the tables fully stocked with a variety of fresh game. This was to be a feast unlike any other. While Abdon's sons were away hunting game, their wives were busy preparing and serving the food. As the week passed, one of Abdon's daughters-in-law, Jael, caught the eye of General Sisera. She was the wife of Abdon's youngest son, Heber.

Sisera was feared throughout the land even more than Jabin himself. Abdon knew a strong personal alliance with the general would be in his own best interest. So, when Abdon learned of Sisera's desire to sleep with the young woman, he saw it as an opportunity to strengthen that alliance and immediately granted his approval. Heber was still out of town, and Abdon instructed his daughter-in-law to say nothing to him.

It wasn't until two weeks after Jabin and Sisera left the city that Jael told Heber what had taken place. Heber flew into a rage at his father's betrayal. "Father, how could you permit such a thing to be done to my wife … and to me?" Heber demanded. "You have dishonored her, and you have dishonored me!"

"I had no choice," Abdon responded. "We must maintain our alliance with Jabin and Sisera at all costs. In the scope of protecting our clan, it was a small price to pay. You must realize that, my son, and move on. Sisera is gone. You and Jael are rid of him. Go on and live the rest of your lives and forget about it."

"How can we possibly forget about it, father?" Heber asked incredulously. "You have robbed us of that which only the two of us were to share – and without any regard for us!"

"Leave our father alone," Heber's brothers interrupted. "He chose to do what was right for our people. You should realize that and be grateful that nothing more was asked of you!"

Heber declared he could no longer be part of a family or clan that had such disregard for one of its members. He decided to take his wife and get as far away from his father and Arad as possible. He and Jael set out that very day on a journey heading north. After twelve days of travel, they came upon a grove of oak trees on a hill overlooking the town of Kedesh. Heber was pleased with what he saw. The ground was fertile, wild game appeared to be plentiful, and he was a far distance from his father. This would be the place he would pitch his tent and raise his family.

Several weeks later, Jael discovered she was pregnant. She quickly realized the baby had been conceived around the time Sisera had slept with her. She had no way of knowing whether Heber or Sisera was the father of her unborn child.

She kept the news from Heber as long as she could. Though her husband had been compassionate when he learned how Sisera had defiled her, their relationship had definitely changed. They had been robbed of the innocence of their intimacy. Though they still loved one another, their physical relationship had grown distant. She was afraid the news of her condition might drive them further apart.

Her decision to conceal the news only made it more difficult when the time came to finally tell Heber. His initial surprise at why Jael had waited so long to tell him quickly paled as he realized the timeframe of the child's conception.

"Am I the father?" Heber haltingly asked.

"I do not know for certain," Jael replied sadly.

A moment that should have been a joyous occasion for this young couple would forever be overshadowed by the primal lust of Sisera and the selfish ambition of her father-in-law.

When the little boy was born, Jael knew instantly which of the men was the father. She loved the little one regardless, but Heber could not bring himself to do so. He refused to give the baby a second look. That day, the child became a wall between Heber and Jael. Though they remained together, there was no longer any expression of love between them … and sadness reigned over their home.

~

12

A NAPHTALITE WARRIOR

During his later years, my grandfather, Shamgar, instructed several young men who were his pupils and proteges. He had become a student of the words and actions of Moses. He saw how Moses had mentored a number of young men, not the least of whom was Joshua. Shamgar decided to do the same and raise up a generation of young men with hearts like Joshua and Caleb – to serve God bravely and humbly, and trust Him fully. He hoped and prayed God would one day use these students to turn hearts back to Him.

One of those young men was a Naphtalite named Barak, son of Abinoam. Barak first caught Shamgar's attention when he rallied the people of his city, Kedesh, to defend themselves against an attack by renegade Aramean warriors.

Years earlier, the Lord had designated Kedesh to be one of six cities of refuge throughout Israel when the land was apportioned to each tribe by Joshua. Those six cities were a portion of the forty-eight cities set aside for the Levites. Kedesh was situated in the midst of the region designated for the tribe of Naphtali. Early on, the city was primarily inhabited by Levites and Naphtalites.

The law of Moses requires anyone convicted of murder be put to death, so these refuge cities were established to provide a safe haven for people who accidentally killed someone. Once inside the city, the assailant would be protected from those attempting to avenge the victim's death. A panel of Levites would judge whether the death had occurred accidentally or not. As priests, the Levites were mediators between our people and God. As such, they were gifted to calmly arbitrate between the attacker and the victim's family, ensuring no further unnecessary bloodshed would occur.

If the Levite panel determined the death was accidental, the attacker could remain in the city of refuge until the death of the high priest in office at the time of the trial. At that time, the attacker could return to his own city without retribution. However, if the assailant left the haven before the death of the high priest, the avenger had the right to seek revenge and kill him.

In the years that followed, the kings of Aramea and Moab had chosen to respect the designation of the cities of refuge and not destroy them. So, the well-fortified city of Kedesh had remained relatively unchanged through the years.

That is, until a large group of Aramean marauders became intent on pillaging whatever treasures the city might possess. They had decided the peaceful city would not be able to defend itself against their attack. However, they underestimated the resolve of the people and failed to recognize the presence of one young man who would valiantly rally his people.

Barak was a skilled shepherd like his father before him. He had learned to stand courageously between his flocks and charging predators, armed only with his staff, his sword, and his knife. No predator had ever gotten the better of him, and his courage was well-known throughout the region.

Barak was also a proven leader. On numerous occasions, he had rallied the other shepherds to join him in facing widespread threats to their herds caused by droughts, fires, floods, and large-scale predator attacks. He became a well-respected voice – not only among the shepherds but also among all the men of the city.

When the band of Arameans threatened to attack, Barak immediately took charge and stationed men, skilled with bows and spears, at defensive stations on the city's walls. He led those who, like himself, were skilled with swords and clubs to strike their invaders. The Aramean warriors were caught off guard and swiftly retreated. Barak and his men pursued them, and only a few escaped death. Before the sun set, peace had been restored in the city.

That victory became legend throughout the land and yielded two significant results. First, it sent a clear message to other renegades that Kedesh was not easy prey and should best be avoided. Second, it made Shamgar aware of Barak right when he was assembling his small group of young leaders to mentor.

Soon after I was born, my grandfather summoned Barak to come to our city. He remained in Ai for fifteen years. My grandfather trained him and helped him further sharpen his skills as a warrior. My grandfather told me on more than one occasion that Barak was the most capable warrior in Israel, a leader of men, and one he would turn to if an enemy ever attempted to attack our people.

After my grandfather died, Barak remained in Ai for a short while, grieving the loss of his mentor and friend before returning to his home in Kedesh. It would be nineteen years before I would see him again.

13

A SUPPORTIVE HUSBAND

My earliest childhood memories include a young Ephraimite boy whose home was next door to mine. We were born the same year and were both our parents' only child. Our parents were not only neighbors but best friends. So, it was no surprise that Lappidoth and I quickly became best friends, too. We believed Jehovah God ordained us to become friends before we were even born.

I never had much in common with the little girls in my village, so I rarely played with them. My mother knew early on that I was definitely my father's daughter! I was more interested in engaging in debate, discovering truth, and settling disputes than I was in keeping a proper home.

Lappidoth and I were very different as well – but we complemented one another. He was gentle. I was somewhat brash – at least more than my mother told me little girls should be. He was cautious. I was daring. There wasn't anything I would not attempt or explore.

One day, Lappidoth and I were out exploring in the hills. I was charging ahead without paying enough attention to my surroundings. As we approached a cliff, I was taken in by the beauty around us and stepped too close to the edge. Suddenly, the ground beneath me gave way. If it weren't for Lappidoth grabbing my arm, I would have fallen to my death into the ravine below. From that day forward, I knew he would always keep a watchful eye on me, while I would always help him take the risks he needed to take.

As we grew older, Lappidoth was the one who analyzed the details surrounding anything we encountered, but I was the one who made the necessary decisions. He always knew more than I did about almost everything, but I could take that information and do something with it.

When we were children, we liked to collect fireflies together soon after the sunset. One day it occurred to me that I was like a bee, and he was like a firefly. He always wanted to make sure the light of truth shone in every situation. As a matter of fact, his name, Lappidoth, means "to shine."

As we became adolescents, I realized other boys in our city were intimidated by me. Physically, I had more strength and greater endurance than most of the young men. They all knew – as did most of the city – that my father would sometimes ask my opinion about a matter over which he was deliberating – whereas most of the boys my age were still idle daydreamers.

But I did not intimidate Lappidoth. He always encouraged me in my pursuits in his gentle way. And I came to rely upon his quiet strength. He was there to humbly support and champion me as I began to achieve greater success. At the same time, I admired his diligence and conscientiousness in everything he did.

Lappidoth clearly inherited his father's carpentry skills. There wasn't anything he couldn't build or do with his hands – and whatever it was, it always reflected the highest level of craftsmanship.

I'm not exactly sure when we knew we would marry, but our parents later confided to us that they had known since we were children. I wasn't in any hurry to get married, and Lappidoth patiently waited for me. I decided he could ask my father's permission to marry me on my twenty-first birthday. The date was set, our wedding feast was arranged, and six months later we were husband and wife.

As the years passed, God blessed us with two daughters. The oldest, Alya, has the nature of her father. Her name means "to go up" – to always take the high and honorable road. It describes her, and her father, perfectly. Our youngest daughter's name, Noya, means "beauty of God." Lappidoth says she is a reflection of me, and I must admit she has much of my nature.

Lappidoth always knew I would follow my father as the next judge of Ai. Truth be told, I was more in doubt than he was. I knew how difficult it would be for the people to accept a woman as judge. But Lappidoth repeatedly reminded me, "The people know you. They have seen you grow up. They know you are just as capable as your father, if not more so.

"Jehovah God has created you for this role. He has gifted you to carry out this responsibility with wisdom and courage. If you doubt your capability, you are actually doubting Jehovah God Himself! Trust Him to bring it about in His way and in His time."

I have come to realize there aren't many men with the strength, humility, and courage to support his wife the way Lappidoth has stood beside me. But God enabled me to marry an honorable man who is just such a husband. In many ways, he is the greatest gift God has given me to accomplish this task. And I know God has placed him beside me to grasp my arm if the ground beneath my feet begins to give way.

~

14

THE ENEMY IS TURNED AWAY AT AI

The day began much like any other day. Alya and Noya were now eight and four, respectively, and had become a great help to me with household chores. I was holding court six days a week for a few hours each morning. I chose to hear disputes beneath a palm tree in a garden on the edge of our city looking westward across the valley toward the city of Bethel.

The palm tree was now referred to as the Palm of Deborah. Usually there were already people waiting for me when I arrived. Often it was a dispute between two neighbors or a disagreement between family members. Jehovah God granted me the ability to settle the disputes and disagreements with wisdom and grace.

Some days the burden of being a judge felt like more than I could bear. God used Lappidoth and my daughters to encourage and refresh me from the heavy weight I felt. I knew they were part of God's provision to lighten my load, just as my mother and I had been a part of His provision for my father.

That particular day, as I was listening to a matter being presented, I noticed unusual movement off in the distance. I initially thought it was a herd of animals migrating through brush in the valley. But soon I realized it was a large group of men. They were advancing toward Ai with speed and purpose. I stopped the proceedings.

"Gentlemen, I must interrupt you! I see a large group of men advancing toward our city, and I do not believe they come in peace," I exclaimed. "One of you run into the heart of the city and sound the alarm, 'We are under attack!' Tell the men to meet me at the city gate!"

The messenger set out with haste while I and two of the other men walked a little closer so we could see the men from a better vantage point. I quickly recognized them as King Jabin's warriors. Though I was aware of General Sisera's attacks on other Israelite cities the past few years, he and his forces had left our region alone. I was told they had avoided the cities of our tribe because of a lingering fear of Shamgar and the fighting men he had trained. Apparently, that was no longer the case!

I instructed the two men with me to continue watching the warriors so they could keep me apprised; I ran to the city gate to organize our men. All the way back, I asked Jehovah God for His wisdom, strength, and favor against this enemy. Lappidoth and the other men were waiting for me when I arrived.

"The Hazorites are advancing on our city from the western valley," I began. "Seal the city gate! Archers, position yourselves on the walls and release your arrows once the enemy is within range. Lappidoth, divide our fighting men into two ranks. One rank will remain here under my command, the other will follow you out of the city to a position in the northern field out of view of the enemy.

"Once the Hazorites have positioned themselves outside of our western gate, you will circle behind them cutting off their retreat. After our archers have reduced their number, the men under my command and I will pour out of the city and attack them head on. They will not be expecting a frontal attack, so we will use surprise to our advantage. Jehovah God will grant us victory today!"

The Hazorites arrived at our gate when the sun was directly overhead. I looked at them from atop the city wall and was surprised at how small their fighting force was – and that they were attacking us from the front at that time of day. Clearly, they were confident we would not fight back. They found, however, that nothing could be further from the truth!

Soon after my men and I initiated our attack, the Hazorites began to retreat. Lappidoth and his men were there waiting for them. God had already made it clear to me we were to show the enemy no mercy. The Hazorites' boldness proved they not only didn't fear us – they did not fear the God of our ancestors.

The fighting was over by midafternoon. Only a handful of the enemy had escaped, and not one of the remaining 500 men who attacked us was alive. By God's grace, we had not suffered a single casualty! God had truly gone before us and utterly defeated our enemy.

I directed Lappidoth to lead a group of men to locate the bodies of the leaders of this assault against us. I wanted to know if General Sisera had led the effort. As I suspected, because of the foolhardiness of the attack, he was not numbered among them. Evidently, this group had been under the command of one of his lesser officers.

Later that night, I called our people to offer sacrifices of thanksgiving to God for His miraculous protection over us. We did so over the next three days – and as we did, we sang songs of praise to our Lord.

In the days that followed, Jehovah God made it clear He was directing me to step forward as a judge over all of Israel to lead our tribes to defeat Jabin's army and free our cities from captivity. I was to follow the example of my ancestors, Othniel and Ehud, and restore peace in Israel. God promised He would go before me and grant us His favor.

I knew what I must now do.

~

15

A COMMANDER IS SUMMONED

~

Two men arrived at my home a week later – one was my husband. He was returning from the city of Kedesh where I had sent him with an important message that I could only entrust to him. He had successfully delivered my message convincing its recipient to respond quickly.

I had heeded the long-remembered words of my grandfather. I called upon his protégé, Barak, to come to the aid of his people. His wrinkles and graying hair reflected the nineteen years that had passed since I last saw him. But he still had the same vigor and vitality of the man I once knew.

"Deborah, judge of Ai, I am honored by the invitation you have extended to me," he said with a slight bow of his head. "Lappidoth told me how Jehovah God granted you a miraculous victory over the Hazorite warriors here in Ai. His hand of favor rests upon you as it did upon your grandfather. There is no question He has called you, not only to be the judge of Ai but to be judge over all of Israel. I am your servant, just as I was to your grandfather."

"You honor me when you compare me to my grandfather," I replied. "You were his faithful servant and the one he often told me we should call on if we ever needed someone to command an army. That hour has come, Barak!

"This is what the Lord, the God of Israel, commands you: 'Assemble ten thousand warriors from the tribes of Naphtali and Zebulun at Mount Tabor. I will lure Sisera, commander of Jabin's army, along with his chariots and warriors, to the Kishon River. There I will give you victory over him.'"[(1)]

Barak looked at me for a moment before answering, *"I will go, but only if you go with me!"*[(2)]

"Why do you make that request?" I asked.

"Because you are the one God has called to be judge over Israel," he answered. "The people must see you as their leader as they did Othniel, Ehud, and Shamgar."

"But it is Jehovah God who is their leader, just as it was in the days of Moses and Joshua," I corrected him. "The people must see Him and give Him all glory – not you and not me!

"Nonetheless, *I will go with you,* as you have requested. *But since you have made this choice, you will receive no honor. The Lord's victory over Sisera will be at the hands of a woman*[(3)] – but they will not be my hands. He will use the hands of another woman to bring honor and glory to His Name – and all the nations will know it is the God of Israel who has defeated His enemy.

"Let us make ready for the journey. We will depart at dawn. And Barak, we will take a short detour as we go."

The next morning, Lappidoth, Barak, and I headed out. God impressed upon me we needed to travel east to the Jordan River before we turned north toward the cities of the tribes of Zebulun and Naphtali.

Just before dusk, we arrived at the plain surrounding the ruins of what had once been the city of Jericho. In front of us was the overgrown rubble of what once were the impenetrable walls of the city. Even the palace King Eglon had subsequently built on top of the ruins had crumbled away.

As we stood there, I could hear the faint echo of people's taunts from the past as they hid behind the city's walls spewing hatred at the Israelite people below. They had underestimated the power of the one true God. They had dared believe their walls and their weaponry could defeat Him.

"It wasn't the might or ability of our people, Barak," I said. "It was the majesty and power of our Almighty God that defeated these people and erased them from this land. No man can take credit for what was done – not Joshua nor Ehud who came after him. Nothing could defeat our God then, and nothing can defeat Him now.

"We do not prepare to fight a battle in our own strength. It is not our muscles that must be fit and ready; rather, it is our hearts that must be inclined toward Him. And if they are, Sisera does not stand a chance!"

As we prepared to make camp for the night, I felt we were standing on holy ground. I knew we were on the Lord's journey. He was going before us. This was all unfolding according to His timing. I slept soundly knowing we were walking in the center of His purpose and His presence.

When the morning sun began to peek over the eastern horizon, we set out on the remainder of our journey. We knew we no longer needed to look at past victories of God; we knew His victory was ahead – victory that would also bring glory to His name.

In two days' time, we arrived in the cities of the tribe of Zebulun where we witnessed how God had gone before us ... once again.

~

16

THE MARCH UP TO MOUNT TABOR

~

The small towns of the tribe of Zebulun had been conquered by Sisera over five years earlier. They were a shell of the towns and villages they had once been. Their young men and women had been taken captive as slaves and sent to Hazor to serve King Jabin. Their parents were left to mourn their loss and to eke out a meager living barely sufficient to pay the taxes Jabin demanded. Periodically, Sisera led his army through the region to ensure the people continued to live in fear.

Barak was better known to these people than I was. He was renowned for his prowess as a warrior and commander. So, it was Barak who introduced me when the people gathered in the first town to see who we were and why we were there.

"People of Kattath, the judges Othniel and Ehud are both well-known to you. God used those men to lead our people to overcome the oppression of our enemies and return us to a life of peace. Your ancestors followed in that pursuit and saw God grant them defeat over their enemies. The judge

Shamgar is also known by you for his heroic victories over the Philistines – keeping them at bay from further aggression.

"You know I fought with Shamgar and considered him to be like a father to me. I now stand before you in the company of Shamgar's granddaughter, Deborah. She has followed in her grandfather's footsteps as the judge of Ai. She has his wisdom and courage. Just last month, she led the people of her city to defeat the forces of Sisera when they attempted to overtake Ai. Every one of those Hazorite warriors was destroyed – but not one of the warriors of Ai was killed. God granted them His great favor!"

I noticed the people began nervously looking at each other. The longer Barak spoke, the more anxious they became.

"God has called Deborah to lead us to defeat Jabin's forces and return our land to peace. Under God's direction, she has asked me to command an army of 10,000 warriors for that purpose, and we have come here to enlist your help. We need every man who is able to fight to join our ranks."

Instead of the resounding cheers we anticipated, the people began to grumble and tell us to leave. "Get out of here," one said. "We don't want you here," another added. "Jabin will have our sons and daughters slaughtered if he finds out we've even listened to you," a woman shouted. "Get away from us and leave this place!"

I had not expected this degree of fear. "We have cried out to God," another said in desperation, "but He will not listen."

"Jehovah God has listened to you!" I shouted. "He has heard your cries – and the cries of the people in the cities throughout this region. He has also heard the cries of your sons and daughters who are being held in captivity. And in response, He has said 'Enough!'

"God has sent Barak and me to tell you He will give you victory over Sisera. Just as God gave our people victory over their Aramean and Moabite oppressors, so shall He free us from these Hazorite tyrants. He will free us from our bondage so we will be free to follow Him and worship Him!

"Turn from the fear and desperation that overwhelms you, and turn back to the God who has time and again freed us from our oppressors. He is our God, and we are His people! Trust Him to lead us to victory and freedom! Join us in this cause that is just! Entrust your sons and daughters to Him, for He will protect them! Do not allow your fear to keep your sons and daughters in shackles any longer! Come with us and see the deliverance of Jehovah God!"

Suddenly, I saw the people's expressions begin to change. I do not believe it was the power of my words; instead, I believe it was the power of our God. They knew His promise was true, and His might was sure. They knew the time of His deliverance had come.

When we left Kattath a few hours later, seventy-five men marched with us. They were a small band of farmers – not warriors – but they were marching behind Jehovah God who was going before us as our banner!

Initially, we received a similar welcome from the towns of Nahalal and Shimron. But as I told them the promise that God had given us, and they saw the conviction of the men from Kattath, they too came around. Our numbers began to multiply as we visited town after town.

Soon, word of our coming outpaced our travels, and the cities and towns began to welcome us with open arms. I realized the victory God had promised was already happening. Our people were already being freed from their bondage. Their gazes were already turning back toward heaven!

We continued to the cities of the tribe of Naphtali. By the time we arrived in Barak's city of Kedesh, there were already 8,000 fighting men in our rank. Shouts of victory awaited us as we marched into Kedesh.

When the time arrived for us to march up to Mount Tabor, there were 10,000 fighting men in our company. We knew that word had already made its way to Sisera, and we knew he would not be far behind.

17

VICTORY IN THE PLAIN

When all was said and done, our fighting force was made up of men from the tribes of Ephraim, Benjamin, Issachar, Zebulun, Naphtali, and the western clans of Manasseh. They had joined in the fight for their common defense and protection. Some, like those of us from Ephraim, had suffered very little at the hands of Jabin but saw it as our duty to come alongside our brothers.

But, alas, not all our tribes had responded in kind. The tribes of Reuben, Gad, and the eastern clans of Manasseh were now settled on the eastern shore of the Jordan River and had completely disassociated themselves from the rest of us. The river was no longer simply a physical boundary, it had become the dividing wall Moses had feared it would become. The eastern tribes had no sense of obligation to come to the defense of their western brothers.

Over the years, the tribes of Asher and Dan – whose regions bordered the Mediterranean Sea – had forged trading relations with the Phoenicians and other Gentile nations, many of whom had alliances with the Canaanites. They feared their involvement in the fight against Jabin's army would sever those relations. Tragically, their desire to feather their nests with the twigs from the rest of the world was more important to them than standing by their brothers.

The tribes of Judah and Simeon considered themselves to be completely out of the fray. Jabin had shown no interest in attacking the cities that far south, so they refused to get involved despite my warning that he could be headed for them next.

We were told Sisera's army was now about 900 iron chariots, 10,000 horsemen, and 300,000 footmen. The bulk of his force was camped outside Harosheth-haggoyim, while the remainder was in Hazor with their king. My spies reported that Sisera and his forces would complete their twelve-mile march and arrive at the Kishon River at the base of Mount Tabor early the next morning.

Barak, Lappidoth, and I knew the odds were against us. Sisera's men were well-trained and well-equipped soldiers. They had been serving and training together for years. Our men were farmers, shepherds, carpenters, and merchants. We didn't have one chariot, let alone 900. We had only a handful of horses. And most of our men had never fought at all, let alone in battle. "Militarily speaking," Barak reminded me, "we don't stand a chance!"

Just then, from outside of my tent, we heard a handful of musicians begin to sing:

"When Israel's leaders take charge,
and the people gladly follow –
bless the Lord!

Listen, you kings!
Pay attention, you mighty rulers!

For I will sing to the Lord.
I will lift up my song to the Lord, the God of Israel.

The mountains quaked at the coming of the Lord.
Even Mount Sinai shook in the presence of the Lord, the God of Israel.

You who ride on fine donkeys
and sit on fancy saddle blankets, listen!
And you who must walk
along the road, listen!

Wake up, Deborah, wake up!
Wake up, wake up, and sing a song!
Arise, Barak!
Lead your captives away, O son of Abinoam!

Lord, may those who love You rise like the sun at full strength!
And may all Your enemies die as Sisera will die!"(1)

I turned to Barak and said, "No, it is Sisera and his warriors who do not stand a chance! Our God fights for us! Let us rise with the sun at full strength and follow Him into victory!"

At sunrise, Barak led our warriors as they charged down the slope of Mount Tabor into the midst of Sisera's forces on the plain beside the Kishon River. They were not expecting us to attack. God used our sudden arrival, together with the chaotic shouts of our warriors, to disorient the Hazorite army. Sisera, his charioteers, his horsemen, and his footmen all panicked.

They trampled over one another as they ran in retreat. Our warriors followed in pursuit the entire twelve miles back to their camp in Harosheth-haggoyim. The fields were soaked with Hazorite blood. And by the time the fighting was over, not a single Hazorite warrior was left alive.

By God's mercy and grace only a handful of our warriors died that day, and a surprisingly small number were wounded. God had given us a miraculous victory – one to be remembered for time and eternity.

As I stood there overwhelmed by what Jehovah God had done, Barak came to me with a report. "Sisera has escaped! He leapt down from his chariot in the heat of the battle and ran away on foot. Several of our men tried to follow him but got caught up in the fighting. He has disappeared. Our men are combing the land between Mt. Tabor and Harosheth-haggoyim, but so far without success.

At first, I could not hide my disappointment. How could we have possibly allowed this man to escape? Why had we not taken greater care to make sure he, of all people, was brought to justice for his crimes? As a judge, I had seen men put to death for much lesser crimes than this man had committed.

But then I remembered God's promise: *"The Lord's victory over Sisera will be at the hands of a woman."*[(2)] And I knew I was not that woman.

I sensed the Spirit of the Lord as He said to me, "Watch and see the victory of the Lord!"

~

18

A GENERAL'S ESCAPE

~

Sisera made his way on foot back to Harosheth-haggoyim just ahead of his retreating army. Apparently, he mistakenly thought our warriors would not pursue his men all the way back to their camp. He planned to rally his forces and lead them back in a coordinated attack to reengage us. But when he saw that most of his army was not going to make it back to camp, he realized the day was lost.

He had a reputation of dressing in a most ostentatious manner – even in battle. Sisera never wanted anyone to be unaware that he was the infamous general of the Hazorite army. Over the years, he had continually added epaulets and medals to his uniform, boasting of his superiority over everyone – except possibly his king.

But now that he knew our forces would be hunting him down, he no longer wanted to call attention to himself. He quickly cast aside all his frills and finery and dressed like a common farmer.

Barak and I were certain he would attempt to make his way to Hazor to reunite with his king and the remaining portion of his army stationed there. Hazor is about thirty miles northeast of Harosheth-haggoyim with a lot of open land between the two cities where someone could easily disappear. Our men began a careful search for him in that direction.

We later learned he had traveled southeast, away from Hazor, toward the town of Beit She'an along the Jordan River. Beit She'an is an Egyptian stronghold in the region. It would appear Sisera was planning to enlist the aid of the Egyptians in defeating our forces and solidifying Hazorite control over our cities once and for all.

The Egyptian administration of Beit She'an had good reason for wanting to hear his proposal. You will recall that King Thutmose II was pharaoh of Egypt when Moses led our people out of bondage. He had led his army to pursue our people with the intent of bringing them back to Egypt. But his effort resulted in his own death when God released the waters to close the dry path through the Red Sea. His son, Thutmose III, became the next pharaoh of Egypt during the time our people were wandering in the wilderness.

Thutmose III was determined to rebuild the Egyptian empire into what it had been before his father led it into ruin. He went about reestablishing control of several regions to the east of Egypt. While Moses was still leading our people through the wilderness, Egyptian forces under Thutmose III's command were victorious over a coalition of Canaanite vassal states in what was called the Battle of Megiddo. Beit She'an became the center of governance over the region they conquered. To this day, they maintained a strong presence in the city.

The Egyptians and our people had remained at peace ever since God had led us into the Promised Land. Thutmose III and the pharaohs who followed him had a healthy fear and respect for the Lord God Jehovah and had no interest in again inciting His wrath. We had stayed clear of one another for the almost 300 years we had been in this land.

But we came to learn that Sisera intended to open those old wounds and convince the Egyptians to extract their long overdue revenge against us. Apparently, the Egyptian leaders weren't opposed to the idea, because Sisera ended up spending several days in Beit She'an discussing a plan with them.

We will never truly know the outcome of his visit, but Barak and I came to believe that Sisera departed the city with a proposal to present to King Jabin. He traveled north along the western shore of the Jordan River on what should have been a two-day journey to Hazor. Evidently, he was convinced his king would overlook his humiliating defeat once he learned of the strategic alliance he had negotiated with the Egyptians.

Sisera was apparently aware that Heber the Kenite had pitched his tent in the grove of oak trees overlooking Kedesh almost two years earlier. He also knew the site was almost halfway between Beit She'an and Hazor. It would provide a comfortable place for him to rest overnight before completing his journey. Sisera remembered the overwhelming hospitality Heber's family had extended to him and King Jabin during their last visit in Arad. He had no reason to believe their welcome would be any less hospitable this time.

I'm certain he believed this would be a safe place to rest and finalize his thoughts on how to best present his grand proposal to King Jabin. He would have also remembered that Heber's wife had been given to him for the night the last time he had seen them. He would have had no reason to believe this time would be any different and he would have relished the thought.

As Sisera approached the hill overlooking Kedesh, he saw the familiar signs of a Kenite encampment in the distance. The familiar blue banners were billowing in the breeze. A handful of animals were visible in an enclosed area beside the main tent. A portion of the land had obviously been cultivated and seeded in preparation for what would soon be a bountiful harvest. Everything appeared to be at peace.

The only sign someone was in the camp was the plume of smoke gently escaping from a cooking fire on the other side of the tent. He probably believed he had outsmarted us by taking a circuitous route, but still he remained cautious. He slowly approached the camp, scanning carefully for lookouts.

Suddenly, a familiar figure stepped out of the tent. She looked the same as when he last saw her. At first, her attention was turned in another direction, but as he continued to walk toward her, she looked up. Her expression confirmed she knew who he was.

~

19

AN UNEXPECTED VISITOR

~

Jael could not believe her eyes. The one who was the cause of all her pain was back. Night after night, her dreams were haunted by how this man had defiled her and how her father-in-law had betrayed her. When she and Heber moved to this place, she thought she had left that pain behind them; but that was not the case. The pain had followed them – and in some ways, had gotten worse.

But she certainly never expected to see Sisera again. Yet, here he was on her doorstep with Heber away from camp leaving her unprotected again. Her husband was gone most of the time now, and she did not expect him back for several days.

Since that fateful night almost two years earlier, Heber seemed to blame her for what happened. He rarely spoke to her, and he would not even look at their one-year-old son. As a matter of fact, he never referred to him as their son – only as *her* son.

But Jael knew none of this was her fault. She had been left to fend for herself by her husband – though she knew he could not have known what would unfold that night. But his treatment of her since then had been unforgivable. And now the one she blamed the most – the one who had not shown any signs of remorse for his actions – was walking toward her. He had ruined her life so he might have one night of pleasure.

Throughout every one of her sleepless nights since then, Jael had called out to Jehovah God for someone to avenge the evil that was committed against her. Repeatedly the Lord reminded her of His promise from the Song of Moses:

> *"I will take vengeance; I will repay those who deserve it.*
> *In due time their feet will slip.*
> *Their day of disaster will arrive,*
> *and their destiny will overtake them."*[(1)]

And she knew her God would be faithful. He alone could take that which was intended for evil and use it for good. In fact, that is why she had chosen to name her son Joseph. The favored son of Jacob had stood tall amid the evil that had been carried out against him by his own family, and she was confident the same would be true for her son.

As Sisera drew closer, an avalanche of emotions welled up inside her. The anger she felt toward him was suddenly overshadowed by fear. He had already demonstrated she was no match for him physically. He had been able to have his way with her despite her efforts to thwart his advances. She knew he was a man without morals who did not fear God. She was afraid for herself but even more so for her son who was fast asleep in the tent. She feared not only for his safety but also that nothing would happen to traumatize him.

She quickly decided her goal was for Sisera to leave her home as soon as possible with as little danger to her and her son as possible. She silently – but fervently – asked God what He would have her do.

The first words out of Sisera's mouth when he reached her were: "Jael, you look as lovely as when I last saw you! Is your husband here as well, or are we to be alone again tonight?"

He made no attempt to hide his intentions. After he made sure they were indeed alone, he asked what she was preparing on the cooking fire. "I am quite famished, and I have been looking forward to a good meal prepared by your delicate hands," he said.

Sisera entered Jael's tent as he spoke. Immediately he saw Joseph sleeping in the cradle on the other side of the tent. "I see you and your husband have been blessed since I was last with you," he said without any thought or concern that the child might be his. "I hope he is a good sleeper, because I have no tolerance for crying babies!"

By God's grace, Joseph did remain asleep for the remainder of that day and throughout the night. As a result, Sisera never gave the sleeping child another thought. Jael went about the work of preparing a meal for Sisera.

While Sisera dined, he began to confide to Jael about the defeat of his army at Mt. Tabor. "It was a minor setback," he lied. But he went on to assure her that he had a plan by which the Hazorites would ultimately prevail. "All I must do is avoid the Israelites who are after me and get to Hazor by tomorrow night," he added.

After he had eaten his fill, he made his intentions clear. Jael was faced with the decision of placing her son in danger or succumbing to his demands. She chose the latter, but she now knew she would be able to use Sisera's anxiety about the Israelites pursuing him to her advantage.

"Come into my tent, sir," she said. *"Come in. Don't be afraid."*[2]

God graciously gave her the strength to endure his physical advances until he had completely exhausted himself. When he no longer had the strength to continue, she covered him with a blanket.

"Please give me some water," he said. *"I'm thirsty."*[3]

Jael gave him milk instead to help him sleep more soundly and covered him with another blanket, so he was good and warm.

"Stand at the door of the tent," he told her. *"If anybody comes and asks you if there is anyone here, say no."*[4]

"I will make sure no one else comes into the tent, sir," Jael replied. "Sleep soundly and rest well."

~

20

AT THE HANDS OF A WOMAN

~

As Jael stood at the entry of the tent, she could see by the light of the moon that Sisera was sleeping soundly. She began to formulate a plan as she watched his chest rise and fall with each breath.

At first, her plan had been to passively submit to his demands so no harm would come to her or Joseph – and then Sisera would be on his way the next morning. But as she watched him sleep, she realized he must be held accountable for his evil actions – against her and so many others. She wondered whether she was being given the opportunity to mete out justice for all his victims.

Her eyes searched the tent for a weapon. Jael saw the bow and arrows Heber had left for her. But she feared what would happen if her aim was off and the arrow missed its mark. Sisera would wake up in a rage, and she and her son would be killed.

She then considered Sisera's sword lying beside him. But she was afraid the sound as she withdrew it from its sheath would awaken him. She was beginning to lose her nerve. Perhaps she should just let her original plan unfold and leave Sisera's punishment to the Israelites.

Then Jael spotted a hammer and tent peg near the inside edge of the tent where Heber had left them. Sisera was sleeping with one side of his head resting on the ground. With one solid blow on the tent peg, Jael could force it through the soft temple on the side of his skull. He would die instantly. But unlike using the bow and arrow, she would have to kneel right next to him to complete the task. What if he awoke just as she was getting into position?

As fear began to grip her, she decided it was too great a risk. But just then, Joseph let out a soft cry. Her mind began to race. What would Sisera do if the baby woke him up? Would he kill her and her son? This was her moment. She had to take the risk to put this to an end once and for all!

Jael swiftly and quietly walked over and picked up the hammer and tent peg. Joseph did not make another sound as she silently crept beside Sisera. In a single motion, she placed the point of the tent peg just above his temple with her left hand and raised the hammer with her right hand. She took a deep breath and held it. Sisera made the slightest of movements, and she knew if she didn't strike now all would be lost!

The metal of the hammer meeting the head of the metal peg shattered the silence in the tent. It was followed by the sound of flesh and bone collapsing as the peg pierced Sisera's skull. His eyes flew open, and his body shook convulsively. Jael thought he was preparing to lunge toward her but realized the peg had gone all the way through his skull and he was now pinned to the ground.

She watched, frozen in fear, as Sisera gasped his last breath. Then just as suddenly as his body had started to convulse, it stopped. Blood began to pool under his head, and his face and mouth twisted into an expression of overwhelming pain.

Jael rolled onto her back and released the breath she had been holding. She lay there for what seemed like an eternity; it was as if time itself had stopped. The sun was just beginning to creep over the horizon when Joseph let out a quiet cry. It was finally over! Sisera's punishment had been delivered. Justice had been carried out – for her and all his other victims.

After covering Sisera with blankets, she began to wash away the spatters of blood from her face, arms, and hands. By then, Joseph was fully awake and made it clear he was ready to eat. As Jael looked down into her son's beautiful eyes, she knew he was the best thing his father had ever done – and now only the best of Sisera would live on.

After breakfast, Jael kept Joseph outside so they could enjoy the warmth of the sunshine and the beauty of the day. As she looked out over the horizon, she saw a small group of men walking toward her. She began to fear they might be some of Sisera's men looking for him. She knew what they would do if they discovered Sisera's body. She thought about fleeing, but she knew they had already seen her, and she could not outrun them.

She started walking toward the men and away from the tent. Perhaps she could redirect them, and they would never discover Sisera's body. As she walked, she turned her head heavenward and asked God what He would have her do.

21

MAY SHE BE BLESSED ABOVE ALL WOMEN

~

"My name is Barak," one of the men said as Jael approached the group. "I am the commander of the Israelite army. We are searching for the commander of the Hazorite army, whom we have defeated and destroyed at the Kishon River. Have you seen a solitary man making his way across this hill?"

"Why do you seek him?" she asked.

"So he can be brought to justice for the evil he has done against our people," Barak replied.

"In that case, I know where you can find him," Jael responded. *"Come, and I will show you the man you are looking for."*[1]

Barak and his men followed Jael cautiously to the entrance of her tent.

"The one you seek, the one named Sisera, is inside my tent," she announced.

Barak and his men drew their weapons in preparation to do battle with Sisera until Jael exclaimed, "Put away your weapons! You do not need them. He can do you no harm."

Jael and her son waited outside as the men entered her tent. "You will find him lying underneath those blankets," she instructed them.

Neither Barak nor his men were prepared for what they saw.

Barak turned to look at the woman in disbelief. "Who has done this?" he asked.

"By God's strength, I did," she replied.

"But how were you able to overpower him?" Barak asked.

"Only by the grace of Jehovah God," she answered.

Barak thought about her answer before he responded. "Deborah – the judge over Israel – told me the Lord's victory over Sisera would come at the hands of a woman. And today, it has come to pass! Tell me your name so our judge and all the people of Israel can celebrate your victory over our enemy."

Jael replied, "Tell Deborah I am one who is a servant of the Lord God Jehovah. I am the mother of this precious little boy who is the best of his father. I am the wife of Heber the Kenite. And today the Lord has blessed me above all women who live in tents. My name is Jael."

She remained outside the tent with Joseph while Barak and his men wrapped and carried away Sisera's body. Before he left, Barak told her I would want to meet her and pay her tribute. Her reply surprised him: "God has already honored me in ways you will never know. He has permitted me to know Him as my Righteous Judge, my Protector, and my Strength. I do not require any further honor."

Later that day, Heber returned home. When he entered the tent, he saw Jael cleaning the blood stain from the floor. "What happened here?" he asked in shock.

"Today God has delivered us from our enemy," Jael replied. She then told him everything that had taken place.

Heber listened in horror at what his wife had been forced to endure yet again. He was overcome with sorrow as he realized his wife and child were vulnerable to such an attack because he had abandoned them. Sorrow turned to repentance as he grasped what his selfishness had nearly cost them all. And repentance turned to a broken and contrite heart as he sought his wife's forgiveness for his abandonment emotionally and physically.

All of that ultimately led to an overflowing admiration for his wife. Jael had done what he had failed to do. She courageously sought justice when he had selfishly run away. She had shown a strength of character that neither he nor his father possessed – and had remained steadfast despite the atrocities committed against her.

That morning, God gave her victory over an enemy and set free that portion of her life. Now, God was giving Heber and Jael victory over the forces that had worked to drive them apart as husband and wife. God blessed all of Israel that day – He restored us as a nation. But He also blessed that Kenite couple that day – He restored them as a family. The nation's restoration had taken place at the point of a tent peg. The couple's restoration had taken place in the shadow of shed blood, and that evening Heber sacrificed one of their lambs to Jehovah God as an offering of thanksgiving.

Barak and those traveling with him returned to our encampment that evening with the body of Sisera. We celebrated the defeat of our enemy and gave praise to Jehovah God. We knew, however, our victory was not yet complete. We planned to lead our forces the next morning to march on King Jabin and his remaining army in Hazor. Once he was defeated, we would truly be free of his captivity.

It would be several weeks before I was able to visit Jael in person and hear her story. I walk in awe of this woman who endured so much and yet walked in the strength and courage that – by her own admission – came solely from Jehovah God. I may be God's judge of Israel, and Barak may be His commander of Israel's army, but Jael is God's champion. She is truly *a woman blessed above all women who live in tents*![(2)]

~

22

PEACE RETURNS TO THE LAND

~

Two days later, we were camped outside the city of Hazor. Our ranks had grown as word spread among our people about God's overwhelming victory at the Kishon River and the death of General Sisera. But the news had also made its way to King Jabin and the citizens of Hazor. Though the number of Jabin's fighting force was still greater than ours, fear was overtaking his heart and the hearts of his people.

He remembered, all too well, how the city of Hazor had been destroyed during the reign of the king whose name he bore. The God of Israel had fought for His people those many years ago just as He had on the day Sisera was defeated. Jabin's army under Sisera's command had outnumbered the untrained Israelite warriors – but their superior numbers had made no difference. The Israelites were victorious because their God was on their side. Jabin had never known fear as king until that day.

To make matters worse, Jabin had relied solely on Sisera to plan and execute their military strategies. Jabin had absolutely no ability in that regard and had little faith in the military commanders who now surrounded him. Sisera had left his least competent commanders behind in Hazor. He had wanted his best with him and never allowed for the possibility he might be defeated.

The king's greatest weapons throughout his reign had been the faithlessness of our people toward our God and our fear of Sisera and his army. In a matter of days, Jabin had seen both of those weapons destroyed – our people had once again been reunited with our God and now feared no one except Him.

That change was also obvious in the atmosphere around our camp. Just days earlier, only a few musicians were sitting around the fires singing, but now most of our warriors were joining in:

"Listen, you kings!
Pay attention, you mighty rulers!
For I will sing to the Lord.
I will lift up my song to the Lord, the God of Israel.

The stars fought from heaven.
The stars in their orbits fought against Sisera.
The Kishon River swept them away.
March on, my soul, with courage.

Lord, may all Your enemies die as Sisera did!
But may those who love You rise like the sun at full strength!"(1)

The next morning as the sun rose, Barak assembled our fighting men to attack the city. I stood on the rise just above them and called out, "This is what the Lord, the God of Israel has said, 'Get ready! Watch and see the salvation of the Lord. Today I have gone before you and vanquished your enemy! Today I have again given you this city!'"

Barak led the charge; I kept a watchful eye as we advanced on the city. We fully expected archers stationed along the top of their walls to greet us with a barrage of arrows – but none came! When the city gate opened, we waited expectantly for a full complement of trained horsemen wielding swords and spears to assault us – but none came! As we passed through the gate, we were prepared for a host of foot soldiers to charge us – but not one advanced on us!

Instead, what we witnessed shocked us – we were surrounded by a sea of death. Soldiers' faces were etched with terror, and it appeared they had turned on one another. The city streets and grounds were filled with blood and the smell of death. The shouts of our charge subsided as the last of our ranks entered the city in complete silence.

I directed Barak to come with me and bring a contingent of men as we made our way to Jabin's palace. When we arrived, there were no guards at the palace doors. Inside, there was no one to prevent us from entering Jabin's throne room. The only thing surrounding us was the same scene we had seen throughout the city.

Barak and I noticed Jabin seated on his throne at the same time. "He has the same expression of terror on his face I saw on Sisera's," Barak said. "But instead of a tent peg through his skull, he has a dagger thrust through his heart – and it appears to have been delivered by his own hand!"

Nothing could ever have prepared us for what we saw that day. We had witnessed great death at the Kishon River, but not like this. Our army never raised a sword or a spear. Our men never cast one blow. We did not lose a single life among our ranks that day. There was no mistake about Who had defeated the Hazorites!

I directed Barak to have our men leave the city and not take anything with them. They were not permitted to take any bounty. This was not our victory. We were not to profit in any way.

Once the men were safely outside the city walls, Barak instructed a few of them to burn the city to the ground; nothing was to remain. God had erased the Hazorites from the face of the earth. It was only by His mercy and grace that it was not us. Our disobedience merited that same punishment. And yet, God had remembered His covenant with His people. Not because we deserved it, but because of who He is!

As we watched the city burn, I knew we were standing on holy ground. In later years, when people spoke of the victories of Deborah and Barak, I immediately stopped them. There is only one name that can be attributed to the events that led to our freedom from captivity ... and that name is Jehovah God.

Peace had now returned to our land.

~

23

RELEARNING HOW TO LIVE IN OBEDIENCE

Our people knew how to live in disobedience to the Lord, but they needed to relearn what obedience looked like. They also had become used to living as a conquered people, but now they needed to be retaught how to live as a free people. You might think that should come naturally for them – but it did not!

The oppression under Jabin had lasted twenty years and our people had turned away from God long before that – so there was an entire generation that had never known anything different. And those who had, had long since forgotten. I knew that leading our people into battle to overthrow their oppressor would be less difficult than what I now faced.

I summoned all the tribal elders, leaders, and judges of the tribes that had joined us in battle to meet me in Shiloh, where the Lord's tabernacle and the Ark of the Covenant had remained since they were placed there by Joshua and Phinehas, the high priest. Uzzi, son of Bukki, was now the high priest. He and his fellow members of the Kohathite clan, which descended from Aaron, Eleazar, and Phinehas, had originally been charged by the

Lord with the responsibility of caring for the Ark and the vessels of worship. In previous decades, the tabernacle had fallen to ruin and our people had abandoned their worship of Jehovah God. It was now time for the sons of Kohath to lead us by carrying out their responsibilities.

Once everyone had arrived in Shiloh, I stood before them and read from the Song of Moses:

"Listen, O heavens, and I will speak!
Hear, O earth, the words that I say!
Let my teaching fall on you like rain;
let my speech settle like dew.

Let my words fall like rain on tender grass,
like gentle showers on young plants.
I will proclaim the name of the Lord;
how glorious is our God!

He is the Rock; His deeds are perfect.
Everything He does is just and fair.
He is a faithful God who does no wrong;
how just and upright He is!

But we have acted corruptly toward Him;
when we act so perversely,
are we really His children?

Is this the way we repay the Lord,
we foolish and senseless people?
Isn't He our Father who created us?
Has He not made us and established us?

For the people of Israel belong to the Lord;
We are His special possession.
He found us in a desert land,
in an empty, howling wasteland.
He surrounded us and watched over us;
He guarded us as He would guard His own eyes.

But soon we became fat and unruly;
we grew heavy, plump, and stuffed!
Then we abandoned the God who had made us;
we made light of the Rock of our salvation.

We neglected the Rock who had fathered us;
we forgot the God who had given us birth.
The Lord saw this and drew back,
provoked to anger by His own sons and daughters."

"But God heard our cries, and He said:
Now I raise My hand to heaven
and declare, 'As surely as I live,
when I sharpen My flashing sword
and begin to carry out justice,
I will take revenge on My enemies
and repay those who reject Me.

I will avenge the blood of My children;
I will take revenge against My enemies.
I will repay those who hate Me
and cleanse My people's land.'

There is no one like the God of Israel.
He rides across the heavens to help us,
across the skies in majestic splendor.
The eternal God is our refuge,
and His everlasting arms are under us.
He drove out the enemy before us;
He cried out, 'Destroy them!'

So Israel, we now live in safety,
in a land of grain and new wine,
while the heavens drop down dew.
How blessed we are, O Israel!
Who else is like us, a people saved by the Lord?
He is our protecting shield
and our triumphant sword!
Our enemies cringe before us,

and He has stomped on their backks!"[1]

I then instructed the leaders to wash their clothing, their bodies, and purify themselves for worship. The next morning Uzzi opened the Book of the Law written by Moses and began to read what was written. When he finished, we all tore our garments and began to call out to Jehovah God in repentance.

Uzzi instructed us to bring seven bulls, seven rams, seven lambs, and seven goats – all unblemished – to be sacrificed as a sin offering. The offering was presented, and the animals' blood was sprinkled on the altar. There could be no forgiveness for our sin apart from the shedding of blood.

After the offering was complete, I led every leader in a pledge on behalf of the people to obey the Lord, with all our hearts and souls, by keeping His commands. We further pledged to remove all the detestable idols that had been erected throughout the land.

When we had done these things, I charged the leaders to gather their tribes and lead their people in a time of repentance, purification, and commitment. There would be no true peace if we did not first make our peace with our Lord. There would be no life without oppression until our people had completely abandoned their false worship and turned back to God.

He had been faithful to us … and now was our time to be faithful to Him.

With that directive, I sent out the leaders to return to their homes and lead their tribes to do as we had done!

~

24

A GOLDEN SHIELD

When Lappidoth and I, together with our fighting men, arrived back in Ai, we were greeted with shouts and cheers. The good news of God's victory had already made its way to the village long before our return. It was a joy to celebrate with our daughters and friends, and know that peace now dwelt throughout our land.

It was with great satisfaction that I returned to my place under the palm tree and began holding court again. Though the matters brought before me were important, they paled in comparison to the battles we had fought. I was often reminded that the same God who had faithfully led us to victory in times of war would lead us to walk victoriously in times of peace. I, in turn, reminded those who came before me that we must seek Him with the same earnestness no matter our circumstances.

I always began a judicial hearing this way: "Neighbors, you have come before me today to present your issue of disagreement. By doing so, you acknowledge I have been given judicial authority over all matters within the city of Ai, and, as of late, throughout all of Israel.

"You acknowledge I have been granted this authority by the elders of this village, by the elders of the tribes of Israel, and by Almighty God Himself. You join me in praying that Jehovah God will grant me His divine wisdom in evaluating the evidence you bring before me, and He will grant me the discernment to apply His wisdom when making my final decision. You agree to accept my judgment as the final word on the matter and to undertake whatever action I so adjudicate."

Regardless of the dispute, the parties coming before me needed to acknowledge my authority and agree to accept my verdict, whatever it might be, before we could proceed. Each side would then present their position of what had taken place.

Because I was the judge over all of Israel, I was in the unique position of hearing disputes from members of different tribes. If I had been only a local judge, I would have needed to be joined by at least two other judges – one from each tribe represented and one from a neutral tribe.

So, it was not unusual for people of different tribes from other parts of Israel to present their disputes before me. Such was the case between Joash of the tribe of Manasseh and Bechorath of the tribe of Benjamin. Both valiant warriors and tribal leaders, they had joined Barak and me in the attack against Sisera's army ten years earlier. They also were with us in Shiloh when we repented as a people before Jehovah God. I knew both to be honorable men.

Joash lived with his Abiezrite clan in the town of Ophrah. He brought his eldest son, Gideon, with him to help present his case. Bechorath lived in Gibeah with the Matrite clan. He also brought his eldest son, Zeror, to help present his case. Little did I know the implications our time under the palm tree that day would have on my family for generations to come.

Joash and Bechorath's cities are divided by the territory of the tribe of Ephraim. Gibeah is near my home in Ai and Ophrah is near the more northern town of Shiloh. As a matter of fact, their dispute started when we were all together in Shiloh following the victory in Hazor. Bechorath had somehow misplaced a golden shield that had been given to him by his grandfather. Joash had found the shield and, after trying unsuccessfully to find its rightful owner, had taken it back home with him.

For ten years, Bechorath had mourned the loss of his family treasure and was convinced the shield had been stolen. During those years, it had become the prized possession of Joash – one which he planned, upon his death, to pass along to his eldest son.

That would have been the end of the story if the two men had not recently encountered one another on their way to the tabernacle in Shiloh. Bechorath saw Joash carrying what he knew to be his shield. A dispute erupted, and neither man would calmly listen to the other. A few days later, they made the journey to Ai and now stood before me ready to plead their case.

I instructed each man to present his claim to me regarding the shield – first Bechorath, then Joash. Their sons were old enough to corroborate their fathers' stories. As the two men quietly listened to one another, it became obvious the shield rightfully belonged to Bechorath. Even Joash's son, Gideon, said, "Father, you must return this shield to this man. It is not yours to give to me; it is his to pass on to his son."

They hadn't really needed a judge to settle their dispute; they only needed to listen to one another. They apologized for having falsely accused each other and embraced as restored brothers and fellow warriors. I invited them to stay the night with Lappidoth and me so we could enjoy an evening meal together. That's when Gideon met my oldest daughter, Alya, and Bechorath's son, Zeror, met my younger daughter, Noya.

It became apparent before the night was over that both young men had more than a passing interest in my daughters – and my daughters were interested in them! I suppose stranger things have happened over the years to bring men and women together. In the case of these young men who would become my sons-in-law, all it took was a golden shield in the hands of a sovereign God!

~

25

A JUDGE TO FOLLOW

~

Forty years have now passed since our victory over King Jabin. Both my daughters are married: Alya and Gideon live in the village of Ophrah, Noya and Zeror live in Gibeah. God has blessed them both with many sons. Noya's oldest son, Abiel, is already married, and he and his wife recently gave birth to my first great-grandson, whom they named Kish.

Lappidoth and I had been married fifty-one years when he died three years ago; a part of me also died that day. Throughout our marriage he had supported me in my role as a judge of Israel. He had been my strength, my confidant, my encourager, and my wise counselor. His presence in my life was a continual reminder that God never calls us to serve Him without equipping us for the task. Lappidoth was an immeasurable part of God's equipping in my life.

But even more than that, he was my partner, my best friend, and the love of my life. I can't begin to tell you the number of times I have gone to turn to him for counsel and companionship over these past three years – only to be reminded he is no longer here. Gratefully, God has been right by my side to help me carry on. But I think I will be joining Lappidoth soon. I grow weaker each day, and I am experiencing great pains in my stomach. Those who have skills in treating such maladies are at a loss as to what more they can do for me. I have asked Jehovah God to continue to give me the days and the strength to finish all He has set before me to do.

Also, by the grace of God, there has been peace in the land these past forty years and our people have greatly prospered. For the most part, we have honored God in our worship and our actions. But I now find that many of our people no longer remember how Jehovah God saved us from the oppression of King Jabin. They no longer recall the death of General Sisera at the hands of Jael or the overwhelming victory over his army on the Kishon River plain or on the streets of Hazor. They have forgotten how we cried out to God for His forgiveness and committed to follow Him.

Instead, our people are now turning away from Him and pursuing their own ways. Many are turning to manmade gods and doing evil in the Lord's sight. Our history as a people reflects this same pattern time and again. God rescues us and we turn toward Him. In our prosperity, we turn away and grow further from Him. We ultimately reject Him and turn to evil. Our enemies see we no longer fear our God and they seize the opportunity to oppress and destroy us. Ultimately, we cry out to God in desperation, and He rescues us.

It has been this way throughout the 367 years since God delivered us from the slavery of Egypt. We repeatedly turned away from Him during our time in the wilderness and here in the Promised Land. And yet, through it all, He has continued to remember the covenant He made with Abraham, extending His mercy to us.

As of late, I have begun to hear reports that marauders from Midian and Amalek are attacking our southern tribes of Judah and Simeon, plundering their animals, and destroying their crops. The Amalekites have been our enemies since the day their warriors attacked our people at Rephidim in the wilderness. God gave us victory over them that day under the command of Joshua, as Moses stood with outstretched arms – assisted by Aaron and Hur – on the hill overlooking the battle. But the hostility between our two peoples has continued to this day.

The Midianites were once our allies. Jethro, the Midianite father-in-law of Moses, helped our people during their journey through the wilderness. But even during the final days of Moses, the relations between our two peoples began to sour, and there has been strife ever since.

I fear the attacks by the marauders will increase in the days to come. As our people continue to pursue their evil ways, I fear the Lord will hand us over to them to seize our attention.

I no longer go each day to sit under the palm tree and judge the disputes between our people. I do not have the strength or physical ability to lead our people against these threatening enemies – and our people currently don't have the will to go up against them. But I am grateful to God there are men and women like Gideon, Alya, Zeror, and Noya that He will use to defeat our enemies and lead us back to Him in the days ahead. Perhaps He will choose one of them to become the next judge over Israel.

Last night as I lay in bed, I heard singing as if by a choir. I do not know where it was coming from, but the familiar words gave me hope:

"When Israel's leaders take charge,
and the people gladly follow –
bless the Lord, the God of Israel!

Listen, you kings!
Pay attention, you mighty rulers!
For we sing to the Lord.
We lift up our song to the Lord, the God of Israel.

Lord, when You set out from Seir

and marched across the fields of Edom,
the earth trembled and the cloudy skies poured down rain.
The mountains quaked at the coming of the Lord.
Even Mount Sinai shook
in the presence of the Lord, the God of Israel.

People avoided the main roads,
and travelers stayed on crooked side paths.
There were few people left in the villages of Israel –
until Deborah arose as a mother for Israel
to lead the people to follow the Lord, the God of Israel.

Then the people of the Lord
marched down behind her *to the city gates.*
Down from Tabor marched the remnant against the mighty.
The people of the Lord marched down against mighty warriors,
And followed the One who went before them – the Lord, the God of Israel.

Wake up again, O people of the Lord,
and again sing a song!
Rise like the sun at full strength
and return to Him,
and follow the Lord, the God of Israel."[(1)]

~

SCRIPTURE BIBLIOGRAPHY

Much of the story line of this book is taken from the Book of Judges. Certain fictional events or depictions of those events have been added.

Some of the dialogue in this story are direct quotations from Scripture. Here are the specific references for those quotations:

Chapter 1

(1) Judges 1:1

(2) Judges 1:2

(3) Judges 1:15

Chapter 2

(1) Deuteronomy 20:16-18

Chapter 5

[1] Joshua 6:26

Chapter 6

[1] Judges 3:19

[2] Judges 3:20

[3] Judges 3:28

Chapter 15

[1] Judges 4:6-7

[2] Judges 4:8

[3] Judges 4:9

Chapter 17

[1] Judges 5:2, 3, 5, 10, 12, 31

[2] Judges 4:9

Chapter 19

[1] Deuteronomy 32:35

[2] Judges 4:18

[3] Judges 4:19

[4] Judges 4:20

Chapter 21

[1] Judges 4:22

[2] Judges 5:24

Chapter 22

[1] Judges 5:3, 20, 21, 31

Chapter 23

[1] Deuteronomy 32:1-6, 9-10, 15, 18-19, 40-41, 43; 33:26-29

Chapter 25

[1] Italicized portions excerpted from Judges 5:2-31

~

LISTING OF CHARACTERS (ALPHABETICAL ORDER)

Many of the characters in this book are real people pulled directly from the pages of Scripture. i have not changed any details about those individuals except in some instances their interactions with the fictional characters. They are noted below as "UN" (unchanged).

In other instances, fictional details have been added to real people to provide additional background about their lives where Scripture is silent. The intent is to provide further information for the story. They are noted as "FB" (fictional background).

Lastly, a few of the characters are purely fictional, added to convey the fictional elements of these stories . They are noted as "FC" (fictional character).

Aaron – brother of Moses, first high priest of Israel (UN)
Abdon – father of Heber, ally of King Jabin (FC)
Abiel – son of Zeror, father of Kish (UN)
Achsah – daughter of Caleb, wife of Othniel (UN)

Alya – eldest daughter of Deborah and Lappidoth, wife of Gideon (FC)
Anath – son of Elad, father of Shamgar (FB)
Asa – brought dispute before Oded to be judged (FC)
Ayala – great-great-granddaughter of Othniel, wife of Ehud, mother of Elad (FC)
Barak – son of Abinoam, protégé of Shamgar, commander of army under Deborah (FB)
Bechorath – father of Zeror, brought dispute before Deborah (FB)
Bukki – son of Shesha, 6th high priest of Israel (UN)
Caleb – son of Jephunneh, one of the original twelve spies, elder of Judah (UN)
Cushan – son of King Jabin (1st), king of Aram, defeated by Othniel (FB)
Deborah – daughter of Oded, wife of Lappidoth, fourth judge over Israel (FB)
Eglon – king of Moab, defeated by Ehud (FB)
Ehud – son of Gera, husband of Ayala, father of Elad, second judge over Israel (FB)
Elad – son of Ehud and Ayala, father of Anath (FC)
Eleazar – son of Aaron, second high priest of Israel (UN)
Elias – brought dispute before Oded to be judged (FC)
Gera – father of Ehud, judge of Benjamin (FB)
Gideon – son of Joash, husband of Alya, fifth judge over Israel (FB)
Hathath – elder son of Othniel and Achsah (FB)
Heber – youngest son of Abdon the Kenite, husband of Jael (FB)
Hobab – son of Jethro the Midianite, Moses's wife's brother (UN)
Hur – Moses's sister's husband (UN)
Jabin (1st) – king of Hazor, defeated by Joshua (UN)
Jabin (2nd) – son of King Tirshi, king of Hazor, defeated by Barak (FB)
Jacob – brought dispute before Oded to be judged (FC)
Jael – wife of Heber the Kenite, mother of baby son – Joseph (FB)
Jethro – priest of Midian, father-in-law of Moses (UN)
Joash – father of Gideon, brought dispute before Deborah to be judged (FB)
Joseph – baby son of Jael (FC)
Joshua – son of Nun, Moses's assistant, second leader of Israel (UN)
Kish – son of Abiel, grandson of Zeror, father of King Saul (UN)
Lappidoth – husband of Deborah, father of Alya and Noya (FB)
Meonothai – younger son of Othniel and Achsah (FB)

Moses – adopted prince of Egypt, a shepherd in Midian, led Israelites out of Egypt (UN)
Noya – younger daughter of Deborah and Lappidoth, wife of Zeror, great-grandmother of King Saul (FC)
Oded – son of Shamgar, father of Deborah, judge of Ai (FC)
Ophrah – son of Meonothai, grandson of Othniel (UN)
Othniel – nephew and son-in-law of Caleb, husband of Achsah, first judge over Israel (UN)
Phinehas – son of Eleazar, third high priest of Israel (UN)
Saul – son of Kish, first king of Israel (UN)
Shamgar – son of Anath, father of Oded, third judge over Israel (FB)
Sisera – general over Hazorite army during the rule of King Jabin (2nd) (FB)
Thutmose II – son of Thutmose I, pharaoh of Egypt during time of exodus (UN)
Thutmose III – son of Thutmose II, pharaoh of Egypt after exodus (UN)
Tirshi – king of Hazor, rebuilt the city (FC)
Unnamed grandfather of Ehud – father of Gera, first tribal judge of Benjamin (FC)
Uzzi – son of Bukki, seventh high priest of Israel (UN)
Zeror – son of Bechorath and Noya, father of Abiel (FB)

~

A FRIEND CALLED ENOCH

KENNETH A. WINTER

DEDICATION

In memory of
all those who came before us
and faithfully walked with God

~

... He was known as a person who pleased God.
And it is impossible to please God without faith.
(Hebrews 11:5-6)

~

PREFACE

~

This fictional novella is the sixth book in the series titled, *The Called,* which is about ordinary people God called to use in extraordinary ways. As i've said before, we tend to elevate the people we read about in Scripture and place them on a pedestal far beyond our reach. We then tend to think, "Of course God used them. They had extraordinary strength or extraordinary faith. But God could never use an ordinary person like me."

But nothing could be further from the truth. The reality is that throughout history God has used the ordinary to accomplish the extraordinary – and He has empowered them through His Holy Spirit.

Enoch was one of those people. Once i started telling people that i planned to write this novella, i have been delighted to hear how many people have been impacted by his story in the Bible. Some have told me how they were challenged to walk with God through his testimony as it is recorded in Scripture. And to be completely transparent, his story is a part of my testimony as well. Lives are still being impacted today by a man who lived over 5,000 years ago!

What makes that even more interesting is that we are told very little about him. He is referenced in only four passages in Scripture: Genesis 5:18-24, Luke 3:37, Hebrews 11:5-6, and Jude 14-15. He is the seventh of the ten antediluvian (pre-flood) patriarchs from Adam to Noah, noted more as a postscript between the stories of Adam and Noah.

Based upon the time frames set forth in Genesis 5, we know that his life overlapped with the lives of all the antediluvian patriarchs, except his great grandson, Noah, who was born after Enoch was gone. It is safe to presume that Enoch would have interacted with his grandfather, Mahalalel; his father, Jared; his son, Methuselah; and his grandson, Lamech. But the Bible does not tell us whether or not he had a close relationship with his older ancestors.

Bear in mind that God had told Adam and Eve to be fruitful and multiply. They did not have a small family. Jewish tradition teaches they had fifty-six sons and quite probably an equal number of daughters. (i think i just heard all the women reading this take a great sigh in empathy for Eve!)

Their children (except Abel) would have many children themselves . . . and so on. Thus, by the time Enoch came on the scene, the extended family would have been in the hundreds of thousands, and possibly in the millions – and growing. So again, we don't know if Adam and Enoch ever actually knew one another. At the very least the stories about Adam would have been passed down through the generations. For the purpose of this story, i have chosen to write it in a way that Enoch and Adam did know one another, and they enjoyed a close relationship.

Also, in Genesis 5 we read: "*Now Enoch lived sixty-five years, and fathered Methuselah.* ***Then*** *Enoch walked with God three hundred years after he fathered Methuselah. . . .*" i have emboldened the word "then," because i take the word literally. i do not believe Enoch was walking with God prior to the birth of Methuselah. Rather, i believe something occurred in his life at the time of his son's birth that caused him to repent and turn – and begin to walk with God. Accordingly, you will see that belief reflected in the story.

Along those lines, there is also a question as to the words "Enoch walked with God." Did they literally walk with one another, or is it a figurative term referencing his close relationship with God? i believe it is both, so you will see that belief reflected in the story as well.

Lastly, i think we often miss the fact that Enoch was a prophet. Jude, the half-brother of Jesus, writes in his epistle that Enoch was in fact a prophet of God. i think that is an important point as we look at his life and also the circumstances surrounding the fact that "*God took him.*"[(3)] There are only two men who ever lived who did not die – Enoch and Elijah.[(4)] Both of them were prophets, and some speculate (myself included) that those men may be the two witnesses who return in the last days as recorded in Revelation 11.

In the Book of Hebrews we read, "*It is destined for people to die once, and after this comes judgment.*"[(5)] The fact that neither Enoch nor Elijah has yet experienced death seems to qualify them for the job of the two witnesses, who will be killed when their assignment is completed. You will see a reference in the story to this possibility.

Lastly, you will find i use references to "The Book of Enoch"[(6)] in the story. The Book of Enoch is an apocryphal book, which means its authenticity is in question. It is most definitely not a part of the canon of Scripture. But Jude actually quotes from the book in his epistle. So at least those two verses[(7)] must be considered as being inspired by God. The apostle Peter also appears to have used a portion of those writings as background for his epistles, 1 Peter and 2 Peter. i do not advocate that "The Book of Enoch" is anything beyond an apocryphal work, but i did determine that a portion of its writings that clearly align with Scripture needed to be included as a part of this story.

i have taken great care to include more background information in this preface than i have in my other books, because i want you to clearly see the line between the factual elements of this story and the portions that are plausible fiction. My desire is that you are introduced to Enoch the person and not merely as a postscript. He was an ordinary man God used – and is still using – in extraordinary ways!

So, i invite you to sit back and enjoy this walk through the life of Enoch and the other characters i believe are an important part of his story. You will recognize many names in the story from the first few chapters of the Book of Genesis. As in all my books, i have added background details about them that are not in Scripture so we might see them as people and not just names.

i have also added completely fictional characters to round out the narrative. They often represent people we know existed but are never provided details about, such as parents, spouses, or children. Included in the back of this book is a character listing to clarify the historical vs. fictional elements of each character.

Whenever i directly quote Scripture during the story, it is italicized. The Scripture references are also included as an appendix in the book. The remaining instances of dialogue related to individuals from Scripture that are not italicized are a part of the fictional story that helps advance the narrative.

One of my greatest joys as a Bible teacher and author is when readers tell me they were prompted to go to the Bible and read the biblical account after reading one of my books; i hope you will do so as well. None of my books is intended to be a substitute for God's Word – rather, i hope they will lead you to spend time in His Word.

Finally, as i have already indicated, my prayer is you will see Enoch through fresh eyes – and be challenged to live out *your* walk with the Lord with the same boldness, humility, and courage he displayed. And most importantly, i pray you will be challenged to be an "ordinary" follower with the willingness and faith to be used by God in extraordinary ways that will impact not only this generation, but also the generations to come . . . until our Lord returns!

1

A SIGHT TO BEHOLD

~

I've been living with Methuselah since my wife, Dayana, passed away. He is a good son and has been a blessing to me from the Lord God Jehovah since the day he was born. His wife, Mira, has been more than patient and gracious with me. I am a terrible house guest; my daughter-in-law never knows whether I will be joining them for meals, which makes food preparations difficult. Truth be told, I have probably been absent from the dinner table more often than I have been there – but she has never once complained.

My schedule fluctuates because I often leave our home to go on long walks. I never know where the walks will lead or how long I will be gone. Those details are all in the hands of the One with whom I walk.

Today began like most every other day. I joined the men who sit at the gates of our village. Just as I have done many times throughout the past 300 years, I declared the words the Lord had spoken to me just the day before:

"The Holy Great One will come forth from His dwelling, and He will tread upon the earth, even on Mount Sinai. He will appear from His camp and appear in the strength of His might from the heaven of heavens.

All will be smitten with fear. The watchers will quake, and great fear and trembling will seize them unto the ends of the earth.

The high mountains will be shaken. The high hills will be made low, and will melt like wax before the flame. The earth will be wholly rent in sunder, and all that is upon the earth will perish.

And there will be a judgment upon all. But with the righteous He will make peace. He will protect the elect, and His mercy will be upon them. They will all belong to God. They will be prospered, and they will all be blessed. He will help them all, and light will appear unto them. He will make peace with them.

And behold! He cometh with ten thousands of His holy ones to execute judgment upon all – to destroy all the ungodly, and to convict all flesh of all the works of their ungodliness which they have committed, and of all the hard things they have spoken against Him."[(1)]

But just like the many times before, instead of remorse and repentance, the response to those words was silence. Those who sat before me acted as if they were deaf and dumb. There was no sorrow over sin. There was no fear of judgment. There was no fear of the Holy Great One!

We live in a day when wickedness prevails. All of creation has seemingly turned away from its Creator, and turned toward all manner and practice of evil. Jehovah God has called upon me to be His prophet, proclaiming His words of coming judgment to this evil generation.

But each day I have found that hearts have become more hardened against the words of the Lord. Each day I become more aware that members of my family are the only remaining righteous ones on the earth – but that is not even true of all of my family.

For some time now, Jehovah God has permitted me to walk with Him. On most occasions I do not see Him in the way you see me. His presence beside me is most often not in physical form – but in many ways, it is even more palpable.

He speaks with me, and I speak with Him. He has invited me to walk with Him in a way similar to how He once walked with the patriarch Adam before the great fall. He tells me what is on His heart, and I tell Him what is on mine. He tells me things that are just for me – and He tells me things that I am to tell others.

We walk and talk for hours. Sometimes we walk to places that are near and familiar. But at other times, He takes me to places that are far away from here – to breathtaking sights that have not yet been corrupted by evil and still display all the pure beauty of His creation.

He once took me to the pinnacle of a mountain range, overlooking what appeared to be an entire region of the earth. As I stood there, I marveled at the Creator's handiwork and His majesty.

As I did so, He said, "Enoch, this is but a glimpse. Your view here is limited. But one day, when you are in My dwelling place, your vision will be unhindered. You will be able to see My creation from My perspective. All that is now dim will be made bright. All that is now unclear will be brought into focus. In the meantime, you and I will continue our walks, because there is so much more I want you to see and do."

That brings me back to today. He and I have walked together for many years and today He took me to a place unlike any other I have ever seen. It is a large city filled with buildings that look very different from those I have seen before. And it is inhabited by people who look very different from me. I know it is a special place, but initially I could not have told you why.

But I am getting ahead of myself in telling my story, so allow me to go back and tell you what transpired leading up to this day. And by the way, if later in your travels you happen to encounter my daughter-in-law, Mira, please convey my apologies for having missed another one of her delicious meals!

2

THE SON OF JARED

~

I am the seventh generation of my family to walk on this earth. It's hard to believe, but every one of my direct ancestors was still living when I was born:

Adam was 622 years old.
His son, Seth, was 492 years old.
His son, Enosh, was 387 years old.
His son, Kenan, was 297 years old.
His son, my grandfather, Mahalalel, was 227 years old.
His son, my father, Jared, was 162 years old.

As you can imagine, I am not my parents' eldest son. Given my father's age at the time of my birth, I am well down the list of children in the order of our birth. Several of my oldest brothers were already grandfathers by the time I was born – making me a great uncle to a multitude of children older than I was.

I had a host of siblings, cousins, uncles, and aunts beyond what anyone could count. The Creator had told Adam and Eve, *"Be fruitful and multiply and fill the earth."*[1] And they had done so! Everyone could trace our ancestral line back to them, but from there the family tree sprouted more branches than a banyan tree. By the time I was born, Adam's descendants had formed countless tribes and peoples living in an equally countless number of villages, cities, and regions. Some said his descendants numbered in the millions.

Though we all shared one common ancestor, we had become a very diverse people, practicing all forms of ungodliness as we each pursued evil desires. We no longer acknowledged Jehovah as our God and Creator; rather, we had become worshipers of different aspects of His creation. Some worshiped the sun and the heavens. Others worshiped the animals of the earth, the fish of the sea, or the birds of the air. Some elevated the lusts of the flesh and declared their godless practices were a form of worship. In seven generations, we had strayed as far away from our Creator as we possibly could. That was true of my father, his father, and most of Seth's descendants.

My father, like the generations before him, was a farmer. My grandfather, Mahalalel, settled his family on an expanse of land along the Tigris River we now call home. He staked out a section of land he deemed to be more fertile than the rest. My father and his many brothers did as well. The land was free to whomever claimed it. But because of the curse of sin, farming – even on this fertile ground – came at great cost.

Jehovah God had told Adam after he and Eve sinned, *"I have placed a curse on the ground. All your life you will struggle to scratch a living from it. It will grow thorns and thistles for you, though you will eat of its grains. All your life you will sweat to produce food . . . until your dying day."*[2] Adam's descendants were now feeling the sting of that curse.

Many of our people turned away from the Creator because of that punishment. They completely lost sight that the Creator was not responsible for the curse; rather, it was the result of Adam and Eve's sin. Our people ignored the fact that a holy and righteous God cannot overlook sin.

To the consternation of our patriarchs, Adam and Seth, my immediate family attributes whatever success we enjoy from the land to the river god. Twice each year, our family presents an offering of the first fruits of the harvest to the river god in thanksgiving – for the plentiful bounty provided and as an act of supplication for continued blessings. My father once told me, "The God of Adam rejected the first fruits offering presented by our ancestor Cain, but the river god has never once been so discourteous." This caused me to grow up with a strong resentment for the Lord God Jehovah.

When I was ten years old, Adam and Eve came to live in our village. Though most of the villagers acted and believed very differently from them, Adam and Eve were still respected as honored ancestors and were warmly welcomed into the village.

I hadn't yet fully comprehended who they were; I just knew they were old. As a matter of fact, they were the most ancient people I had ever seen! I knew we were somehow related, but it was still too confusing for me to understand. My parents instructed me to call them "Abot" and "Matre" out of respect for their position in our family as patriarch and matriarch – though I didn't really understand what those titles meant either.

They situated their home near ours, so I saw them often. My parents frequently invited them to have a meal with us. Abot would always tell me stories about the ancient days. He was joyful as he shared some of the tales, but other stories made him sad.

Though most of his accounts were from long ago, he made it seem like they happened yesterday. I had never heard anyone speak of the Creator with such affection. It was as if the Creator was his dearest friend – a friend he had betrayed.

The more time I spent with Abot and Matre, the more I was drawn to them. My relationship with my grandfather, Mahalalel, and my great-grandfather, Kenan, had never been close. But I wanted to be around Abot and Matre continually so I could hear more of their stories.

One day Abot asked me, "Enoch, do you know why Matre and I came to your village?"

When I shook my head, he replied, "Because the Creator wanted me to tell you these stories. He wants you to know about Him . . . and even more importantly, He wants you to know Him!"

3

THE VERY BEGINNING

~

Abot began to tell me his personal story. "Unlike you, Enoch, I have no childhood memories. I never needed to learn how to walk, how to talk, or how to care for myself like you did. I had no parents to teach me like you do. The Lord God Creator formed my body from dust and, like everything else He created, He did so perfectly.

"I had no blemish, no defect, and no deficiency," Abot continued. "The Creator didn't have to experiment by creating earlier versions of me until He found the one that best suited His plan. He had me in mind before He created time itself.

"But the true miracle of my creation is not that He created me from the dust of the earth. The true miracle is that I am the product of His breath. He breathed into my nostrils – filling my mind, my will, my emotions, and my spirit with His likeness. Unlike any of His other creations, He created me in His image and gave me charge and dominion over all His other creations.

"My first memory is the moment I opened my eyes and took in my first breath. There I was, face to face with my Creator. Enoch, imagine if you can, what it was like to enter the world – not through your mother's womb – but as a fully grown man with the capacity to think, feel, and communicate as an adult from the moment of your first breath," Abot told me.

"From that moment, I was able to speak to God, and I was able to understand Him when He spoke to me. And I am mindful that the Creator gave me that gift of language, first and foremost, so I could communicate with Him. Yes, I would later use language to talk with others, just like you do, but primarily He intended I use that gift to speak with Him – in praise, in worship, and in fellowship. That was a truth I would soon fail to consider.

"On the first day of my life, God planted a magnificent garden filled with all sorts of beautiful trees, many of which produced delicious fruit. Many of those trees and bushes you have here in your garden. But there is an important difference – it was a perfect place, without any thorns or thistles. He told me to tend to it and care for it. Never before had there been such a garden, and never before had there been anyone to look after it. The One who created the garden instructed me how to nurture it – perfectly and lovingly – in the same way He had created it.

"But then He added this warning: '*You may freely eat any fruit in the garden except fruit from the tree of the knowledge of good and evil* in the center of the garden. *If you eat of its fruit, you will surely die.*'[1]

"He showed concern for His garden, but He showed even greater concern for me. He said, '*It is not good for the man to be alone. I will make a companion who will help him.*'[2] He proceeded to form every kind of animal and bird from the dust, just as He had created me. But He did not breathe into their nostrils. Rather, He simply spoke a word and each one awakened. He placed them before me and told me to choose an appropriate name for each one. But first, He gave me a name – Adam – meaning 'son of the earth.' Since He had created me from dust, it was certainly fitting!

"As the birds and animals passed before me," Abot continued, "I observed there were two of every kind – male and female. Each one had a companion, but I realized there was no companion for me. But I knew the Creator had not made an oversight. Nothing catches Him by surprise! He had always known I would need a companion of my own kind. In His wisdom, though, He wanted me to come to that same conclusion. He did not want me to take my companion for granted, but rather recognize my need and know He specifically created her for me.

"The Lord God directed me to lie down, and I immediately fell asleep. It was the first time I had ever slept – and it was a deep sleep. The Creator opened my side and removed one of my ribs, using it to create the woman He also patterned in His own image. Then He closed up my side, leaving a faint scar.

"See, Enoch, the scar is right here," Abot said, opening his cloak.

"It's not a blemish; rather, it's a reminder for Matre and me that she was bone of my bone and flesh of my flesh. I did not experience any pain or discomfort during or after the Creator's surgery. I awoke feeling rested and fully restored.

"As soon as my eyes fell upon Matre, I was overwhelmed by her beauty and gentleness. I exclaimed, '*At last! She is part of my own flesh and bone! She will be called "woman," because she was taken out of a man.*'[(3)]

"The Lord God Creator blessed us both saying, '*Multiply and fill the earth and subdue it. Be masters over the fish and birds and all the animals. I have given you the seed-bearing plants throughout the earth, and all the fruit trees for your food. And I have given all the grasses and other green plants to the animals and birds for their food.'"*[4]

4

WE WALKED WITH HIM . . .

~

Abot continued with his story. "As that first day came to an end, God looked over all He had created and announced it was excellent in every way. He had labored six days to create the light and the darkness, the earth and the waters, food for us and the animals, work for us to do, and the gift of companionship with each other. He declared the seventh day would be a day of rest.

"But even more than that, He had granted us fellowship with Him. Our Creator made us with the desire to have a close relationship with Him, and He desired to have fellowship with His creation. He proclaimed the seventh day would be set aside for rest and a special day of fellowship with Him. He declared it to be holy.

"During those early days, the Lord God would come walk in the garden with Matre and me in the coolness of the evening. He walked with us and talked with us and reminded us we were His creation, and He was our Creator. He was the only parent we would ever have. He never tired of our questions, patiently answering each one. We looked forward to those walks, and I believe He did as well!

"Matre and I never grew weary of laboring in the garden. Our fellowship with God gave our lives purpose, and our work gave us meaning. Our walks with God enabled us to know Him more and know each other more intimately. Words will never adequately describe what our lives were like in those early days.

"But one day, everything changed. Matre and I were tending to different areas of the garden when she was approached by the serpent. He was the most beautiful of all creatures. I had marveled at his beauty and cleverness the day he was created. He was one of the few animals given the ability to speak, and on previous days Matre and I were delighted when he would talk with us.

"But on this day, the serpent was different. He was under the control of another being – one called Lucifer. Matre did not know the serpent was under Lucifer's influence. Nonetheless, we both knew the words being spoken by the serpent were contrary to God's commands.

"'*Did God really say you must not eat any of the fruit in the garden?*'(1) the serpent asked Matre.

"She replied, '*Of course we may eat it. It's only the fruit from the tree at the center of the garden that we are not allowed to eat. God says we must not eat it or even touch it, or we will die.*'(2)

"'You won't die!' the serpent hissed. '*God knows that your eyes will be opened when you eat it. You will become just like God, knowing everything, both good and evil.*'(3)

"Enoch, I need you to understand that Matre knew what the serpent was telling her was contrary to God's command. She knew God had told us not to eat from the tree under any circumstances. But the fruit looked inviting. And now the serpent was telling her it would make her wise. At that moment, the creation decided she knew better than her Creator.

"And so did I, because when Eve extended the fruit to me to eat, I also knew it was contradictory to God's command. The moment we took a bite, a sense of shame washed over us both. We suddenly became aware that we were naked, and we reached out for leaves and branches to cover ourselves.

"We knew what we had done was wrong. We had never before experienced feelings of guilt and shame. And when we later heard the Creator approaching, we hid from Him. Until that moment, we had never considered hiding from Him. We had always run to Him!

"I heard the Lord call out, '*Adam, where are you?*'(4)

"As He approached the spot where I was hiding, I replied, '*I heard you, so I hid. I was afraid because I was naked.*'(5)

"'*Who told you that you were naked?*' the Creator asked. '*Have you eaten the fruit I commanded you not to eat?*'(6)

"'*Yes,*' I replied with my eyes averted from the Creator, '*but it was the woman You gave me who brought me the fruit, and I ate it.*'(7)

"I was sorry as soon as I uttered those words. I was blaming Matre – my companion, my wife, and my helpmate. How could I even consider shifting the responsibility to her? She had not made me disobey God; I had made that decision on my own.

"And what's more, the Creator had charged me with the responsibility of tending to the garden – not her. And He had specifically told me not to eat the fruit of that tree. If anything, I should have kept her from doing so. But instead, I had disregarded the Creator and done what was right in my own eyes. Who was I to blame Matre for my disobedience? I now felt even more ashamed!

"The Creator turned to Matre and asked, '*How could you do such a thing?*'[8]

"Then she did the same thing I tried – she passed the blame off to someone else! '*The serpent tricked me!*' she replied. '*That's why I ate it.*'"[9]

Just then my mother called out, "Enoch, it is time for you to go to bed!"

5

. . . UNTIL WE COULD NO MORE

I couldn't wait to find Abot the next morning so I could hear the rest of his story. As soon as I saw him, I asked, "What happened? What did the Creator do?"

He told me to come sit beside him. Once I was settled, he continued. "The Lord God Creator turned to the serpent and said, '*Because you have done this, you are cursed more than all animals, domestic and wild. You will crawl on your belly, groveling in the dust as long as you live. And I will cause hostility between you and the woman, and between your offspring and her offspring. He will strike your head, and you will strike His heel.*'(1)

"Immediately, the serpent's legs disappeared, and he began to slither in the dirt. He opened his mouth to speak but the only sound he could make was a hiss. An animal that had been the most beautiful had become the most despised. He quickly slithered away into the shadows.

"God turned to Matre and said, '*I will sharpen the pain of your pregnancy, and in pain you will give birth. And you will desire to control your husband, but he will rule over you.*'"(2)

"So is that why my mother cried out in pain when she gave birth to my little sister?" I asked.

"Yes, it is," Abot replied, then continued. "The Creator then turned to me and said, '*Since you listened to your wife and ate from the tree whose fruit I commanded you not to eat, the ground is cursed because of you. All your life you will struggle to scratch a living from it. It will grow thorns and thistles for you, though you will eat of its grains. By the sweat of your brow will you have food to eat until you return to the ground from which you were made. For you were made from dust, and to dust you will return.*'(3)

"The Creator then called out for two beautiful animals grazing nearby to come to Him. They looked lovingly into the eyes of their Creator who told them He would require they sacrifice their lives so Matre and I could be clothed in their skins. Both animals responded by saying, 'Whatever You require of us, we will do. Because we know that You love us and will only do what is best for us!'

"With that, they laid down their lives, and death entered into this world. The Creator clothed Matre and me in their skins. I wept as I wrapped their skins around us, knowing that our sin had cost those beautiful creatures their lives, and that species would no longer exist because of their sacrifice for our sin. But that was only the beginning. I had not yet fully grasped the breadth of the consequence of our sin.

"My attention was turned back to the Creator when I heard Him say, 'Adam and Eve *have become like Us, knowing both good and evil. What if they reach out, take fruit from the tree of life, and eat it? Then they will live forever!*'(4)

"I knew the Creator wasn't asking me; rather, He was speaking aloud to Himself. And I had come to realize that whenever He spoke about Himself, He often used a plural pronoun. He had explained during one of our walks that there was more to Him than I could see. He said He was one God in three persons – Father, Son, and Holy Spirit. But I must confess that at the time, I couldn't quite comprehend what He was saying. And Enoch, I'm not so sure I completely understand it today.

"What I do know is the Lord banished Matre and me from the garden that day. He stationed His angels at the gates guarding the entrance. We would never be permitted to return. As the years passed, we found we could no longer remember where the garden was.

"We were exiled from the garden because of the tree of life. That tree was also located in the center of the garden but, unlike the tree of the knowledge of good and evil, we had been permitted by God to eat its fruit. But now that would no longer be the case. A consequence of our sin was that we – together with the animals and all those who came after us – would die a physical death. Our physical bodies would no longer live eternally. Death, disease, and decay would now be as much a part of our lives as birth. Everything had changed because of our disobedience!

"We eventually made our way to another parcel of land, which became our new home. We lived there until we came here. I cultivated it as the Creator had taught me, but it never even approached the beauty, splendor, or bounty of the garden. It provided us with some food, but we soon realized we needed to supplement our diets with meat – which meant that more animals and birds would need to die for our sakes. They were now all reproducing more of their kind, and their number was increasing.

"Not long after, Matre came to me with the news she was pregnant. It was time for *our* seed to grow in number! Matre had many questions about childbirth, and we both had more questions than ideas about raising a child. Without question that task would be greater than any other the

Creator had placed before us to do. But, by His grace, He assured us He would be there to guide us along each step. And He was."

It was time for me to join the others and go work in the fields. As I left, Abot said, "I will continue my story the next time we are together."

6

THE SINS OF THE FATHER . . .

My brother, Shep, was born one year after I was. With such a large family and such a wide age disparity between siblings, we usually had closer relationships with brothers and sisters nearest our age. Shep and I enjoyed the closest bond while growing up.

We enjoyed exploring the land. When we were young, we had fewer responsibilities than our older brothers. That gave us more time to explore the hills and the valley, as well as enjoy an afternoon swim in the river – a practice that continued even as we got older.

Though Abot often told me the beauty of the land paled in comparison to Eden, I still marveled at its magnificence. Even as a boy, I believed that a Master Creator had formed each delicate flower, each majestic tree, and each rolling hill. I was particularly in awe of the vibrancy and breadth of colors, each one as rich and brilliant as the other. I found myself wondering what everything would have looked like without all those spectacular colors – but I was thankful that would never be a concern.

My father taught us to thank the river god for all the beauty. But the more I listened to Abot, the more I began to think my father might be wrong. However, I decided I would continue to keep an open mind and listen to them both. Several weeks passed before Abot was able to continue with his story.

"Our firstborn son was also the first baby to *ever* be born," he told me. "Matre had seen many of the female animals in the garden give birth, but she had never seen another woman do so – nor was there another woman to ask. At the time of our son's birth, he was only the third human on the face of the earth.

"His birth was not without its pain and travail. After the birth, Matre informed me, 'God told me I would bear children with intense pain and suffering, but until I experienced it, I did not fully understand just how difficult it would be. But the Lord God Creator did not abandon me in my hour of need; with His *help, I brought forth a man!'*[(1)]

"We named him Cain, and for the first year of his life, he was our only child. His 'firsts' as a child were our 'firsts' as parents. His first steps were a victory for us. We learned there would be times he would fall down, but it would all be a part of his learning how to walk on his own. The Creator told us it was an important lesson for us – and him – to learn.

"Next came his first words. We watched as he struggled to learn to speak. Having never had that struggle ourselves, we could not completely understand. We had expected him to be able to speak from the moment he was born – just as we had done. But we quickly realized we needed to patiently teach and encourage him.

"Cain was almost one year old when our daughter, Awan, was born. Matre again experienced the pain and difficulty of childbirth, but this time she had a better idea of what to expect. It wasn't long before Cain considered himself his baby sister's protector. They were close, like you and Shep, from the very beginning. But that wasn't true of his feelings toward our next child, Abel.

"Cain was almost two when Abel was born. Even at that age, I could see a change in Cain. His attitude toward his baby brother was different from when Awan was born – maybe because he was younger then, but more than likely because Awan was a girl. Up until then, Cain had been my only son. But almost from the moment Abel was born, Cain saw him as a rival who inserted himself into the exclusive relationship Cain had enjoyed with me.

"I did everything I could to assure Cain of my love and the special place he would always hold as my firstborn son. Still, as he grew older, I observed his tendency to posture himself in a more favorable light than his brother. For example, I was blessed he wanted to learn everything I could teach him about being a good farmer, but I also knew part of his motivation was to be better at it than Abel.

"As time passed, Matre gave birth to many more children. On three occasions, she gave birth to twins. As a result, our family was growing rapidly. By the time Cain was sixteen, we had nineteen children. But it grieved me as a father that Cain continued to feel the need to compete with his brother. Gratefully, I never saw any sense of competition from Abel. Rather, he desired to have a close relationship with his older brother.

"As Abel got older, he chose to become a shepherd. I believe it grew out of his love for animals and his ability to care for them. But I also believe Cain's penchant for turning everything into a competition may have played into it. Though Abel never said, I wondered if he became a shepherd so his brother would not feel the need to compete as farmers.

"I was proud of both my sons in the way they went about their work. One day when Abel was fourteen years old, I remember telling him, 'Abel, you remind me of our Lord God Creator. You care for your flock, just as He cares for us. You protect each one, and when they stray, you seek them out. You do not leave them or abandon them. I am proud of you for the choice you have made and for the way you attend to your duties.'

"Abel received my words humbly, but I saw Cain out of the corner of my eye as he scurried away. Apparently, he had heard what I told Abel."

7

. . . AND THE INIQUITY OF THE SON

~

As I thought about Cain and Abel, it made me reflect on my relationship with Shep. I'm grateful that I never felt like he and I were in competition for our father's approval. Of course, I wasn't the eldest son. Perhaps that would have caused me to think differently. However, I don't believe so.

I saw the sadness in Abot's eyes as he continued with his story. "Later I told him, 'Cain, I am proud of both of you! My pride for one does not diminish my pride for the other. Don't resent what I have said to your brother. I have told you many times about how proud I am of you!'

"But sadly, Cain's resentment for Abel did not diminish. The sin nature that now dwelled within all of us fostered a selfish ambition in Cain that only increased. Nothing Matre and I did made any difference.

"When Cain was eighteen, Matre and I sat down with him and Awan and told them it was time for them to become united as husband and wife. The

Lord God Creator had instructed us that when our sons came of age, they were to leave us and be joined to a woman. Awan and Cain had been close all their lives, and they had always known this day would come. They would now be the first of their brothers and sisters to marry. They were now the center of attention – which Cain relished.

"Over the years, Matre and I had become skilled in making clothing from the skins and hair of animals for our family to wear. Awan and two of her sisters had also developed that skill. We all worked together to make the most beautiful clothing we could for Awan and Cain to wear for their marriage celebration. The Creator Himself officiated over the exchange of vows.

"The events surrounding the marriage distracted Cain from his resentment toward his brother – at least for a little while. A short time later, the Creator told me the time had come for us to present a harvest offering to Him as an expression of our thanksgiving for His provision. I instructed Cain and Abel to gather the offering, and I reminded them that this was not a competition. 'Bring the best,' I said, 'because the Creator is worthy of the best!'

"Cain immediately set out collecting the best of the firstfruits of this year's harvest, but it was obvious he did see this as a competition with his brother. When the day for the presentation arrived, he proudly paraded his offering before God. He had enlisted several of his younger brothers and sisters to help him carry it all. The quality of the fruits and vegetables was quite impressive. When Cain bowed his head before the Creator, I watched him glance up to make sure God looked pleased with what he had brought.

"The Creator told him to stand to the side so Abel could present his offering. Abel walked in leading several of his spotless lambs. I think I saw Cain chuckle when two of the lambs bleated disrespectfully as they were led before the Lord. Cain obviously thought Abel's offering was inferior. Abel tied the lambs to a branch and bowed his head without a word.

"Everything was silent as God seemed to evaluate the two offerings. Suddenly, He spoke to my younger son: 'Abel, the day your father and mother sinned in the Garden of Eden, I slew two beautiful animals so the nakedness of your parents could be covered. The blood of those precious animals was shed so your parents' sin could be covered. Their blood was the true gift ... a sacrifice ... given by those two spotless animals.

"'Today, you have brought these unblemished lambs before Me from the best of your flock. You have presented them to me for their blood to be shed as an offering of thanksgiving to Me. You have sought nothing in return, just like these lambs, humbly and reverently presented to Me. Abel, I accept your offering of thanksgiving.'

"Then the Creator turned toward my older son and said, 'Cain, you are the firstborn son of Adam. You have all the rights and responsibilities that your position in birth entails. And yet, you have lived most of your life in the shadow of envy and resentment toward your brother. The serpent tempted your mother – and she in turn tempted your father – with the desire to have that which I had told them they could not have. They responded to that temptation with the same envy toward the fruit for what they thought it would bring, and resentment toward Me because I had told them they could not have it.

"'As a result, sin was birthed in their hearts and in this world. It is the same sin that dwells within your heart. That sin has tempted you to envy and resent your brother. It has led you to bring these fruits and vegetables before Me – not as an offering of thanksgiving – but as a means through which you hoped to validate your own selfish desires. You have come in the hope I will honor you above your brother.

"'Cain, I reject your offering because you have brought it to Me with iniquity in your heart. Turn from your wickedness and turn toward Me. Your enemy, the deceiver, lies in wait for you, just as he did your parents! Do not heed his voice!'"

~

8

WHY, BROTHER?

There were so many questions I wanted to ask Abot, but I decided to remain silent and let him continue with his story.

"I watched my son's horrified reaction to what the Creator said. I hoped he would be remorseful and repentant; but instead, he took the Creator's rebuke as another way Abel had bested him. He obviously blamed his brother for the reprimand he had received.

"The Lord God looked at Cain and asked, '*Why are you so angry? Why do you look so dejected? You will be accepted if you respond in the right way. But if you refuse to respond correctly, then watch out! Sin is waiting to attack and destroy you, and you must subdue it.*'(1)

"Cain abruptly turned and walked away, not even taking time to collect the offering he had brought God. He was embarrassed. His offering had been rejected, and he'd been rebuked in front of his family – including his younger brothers and sisters who looked up to him. I knew my son well enough to know he wasn't walking out in sorrow over his sin, he was seething with anger.

"I knew he wouldn't receive anything I said to him at that moment. I looked over at Awan, and she obviously thought the same. She knew when her husband got like this, no one could talk to him. And none of us had ever seen him this angry.

"I later learned what was going through Cain's mind after he stormed off. He apparently began to consider what his life would have been like if Abel had never been born. The more he thought about it, the better he liked it. Suddenly, a horrifying thought washed over him, and he began to warm to the idea.

"'Yes, that is the solution to my problem,' he thought. 'With Abel out of the way, everyone will pay me the honor and respect I am due. It will be as if he never existed.' At that moment, he heard a hissing sound from the corner of the room, he later told me, and then he saw something slither across the floor and out the door. Quickly, the tail of the serpent disappeared.

"Cain stayed by himself the rest of that day and night, but the next morning he rose early and set out to act on his plan. As he expected, Abel was already awake when he found him. His brother had always been the earlier riser. Cain approached him and said, 'Abel, I behaved badly yesterday before the Creator, our parents, and all of you. I was so surprised by what the Creator said I didn't know what to do. You've always understood Him better than I do. I wondered if you would be willing to help me make amends and do what I need to do.'

"'His ways are simple,' Abel responded, 'but sometimes they are difficult to live out. Not because of what He expects, but because of the pull within us to go our own way – just like Mother and Father did in the garden. They gave into that voice and did what they knew was wrong. And as a result, so do we. But the Creator is faithful to forgive us if we will repent of our ways and seek His forgiveness. That is what you must do, Cain. You must go to Him and repent and seek His forgiveness.'

"'I am the older brother,' Cain responded. 'I know these things – but sometimes I don't want to do what I know I am supposed to do. Will you go with me as I go to the Creator? Having you with me will give me the added courage I need to do what I must.'

"'It doesn't take courage, brother,' Abel replied. 'It takes a broken and contrite heart. But I will go with you if that is what you want.'

"'It would be a great encouragement to me,' Cain said. 'I saw the Creator heading toward the riverbank for an early morning walk when I was on my way to find you. We should be able to catch Him there if we hurry.'

"Cain began to lead the way, and Abel followed close behind. However, when the bushes formed a fork in the path, Cain went to the right. Abel quickly called out, 'No, brother, the riverbank is this way. We need to go to the left.'

"Abel made the correct turn, and Cain quickly made the adjustment to be right where he had always intended – following closely behind Abel. With the bushes surrounding them on both sides, and Abel's attention fixed on the path ahead, Cain removed the stone blade he was carrying at his waist. With one fluid motion, he reached around and held Abel's forehead with his left hand, and drew the blade across his brother's throat with his right.

"Abel's head fell back toward Cain's chest as his body collapsed. With his final breath, Abel looked up into Cain's eyes and mouthed, 'Why, brother?'"

Up until that point, Abot had been trying to maintain his composure as he told me what happened, but it became too much, and he began to weep. "My precious son Abel was murdered at the hands of my firstborn son!" he cried out.

I knew there was nothing I could say or do that would console Abot. The grief and sorrow were as fresh at that moment as they had been all those many years before.

9

THE OUTCAST

~

A short time later, Abot was able to continue with his story. "As we later discovered, Cain buried Abel's body and covered his grave with underbrush, believing we would never find it.

"The sun was just beginning to rise higher in the sky as Cain returned to our homesite. We were now all awake and just beginning the workday. We were surprised to discover the Creator standing in the center of our camp. It was highly unusual for Him to join us at that time of day. As soon as He saw Cain, the Creator called out, '*Where is your brother? Where is Abel?*'[(1)]

"Cain knew the Creator knew all things, but still he attempted to deceive Him. He answered, '*I don't know! Am I supposed to keep track of him wherever he goes?*'[(2)]

"Just then Matre and I walked into the middle of the camp and stood beside the Creator. We could tell from His presence and His questions that something was wrong. We strained to hear Cain's answer.

"'*What have you done?*' the Lord demanded. '*Listen – your brother's blood cries out to Me from the ground. You have defiled the ground with your brother's blood. No longer will it yield abundant crops for you, no matter how hard you work. You are hereby banished from this place. From now on you will be a homeless fugitive on the earth, constantly wandering from place to place.*'"[3]

"It was as if the blade of a knife had been plunged into my heart as I struggled with the reality of God's words!" Abot exclaimed, as tears again formed in his eyes.

"'I am the firstborn son, my Lord,' Cain cried out. '*My punishment is too great for me to bear! You have banished me* from my world as I have known it and *from Your presence. You have made me a wandering fugitive. All who see me will try to kill me . . .* today and in the days to come!'[4]

"'*They will not kill you,*' the Lord replied, '*for I will give seven times your punishment to anyone who does.*'[5]

"The Lord then placed a mark on Cain's face as a warning to anyone who might try to kill him. One by one, all of our family turned our backs on him, the last being Matre and me. Our hearts were broken. We had lost two sons that day – as well as a daughter – as Awan followed her husband out of the camp.

"The journey of sin led them farther and farther away from us that day, as Cain and Awan made their way east. They did not know where they were going, but they knew they must place a considerable distance between themselves and us. Awan was expecting a child when they left our camp that day. She would soon give birth to our first grandson, whom they would name Enoch – just like you! When I look into your eyes, I often think of him – my first grandson whom, like the rest of Cain and Awan's children, I have never met.

"Awan had no one to help her when the time came to deliver the baby. Matre had been looking forward to helping her with the delivery because Awan had assisted her with the deliveries of many of our children.

"The journey of sin not only led them farther away from us in physical distance, but it also led them further away relationally from the Creator. Cain never repented of his sin; rather, he chose to grow in his wickedness, as did his offspring.

"Cain sired a multitude of children. Cain and Awan continued to have children until they were both well over 100 years old. Those sons and daughters were given to one another in marriage and each of them gave birth to large families. By the time Matre gave birth to our son – your patriarch, Seth – six generations had descended from Cain and Awan, with their extended family numbering in the tens of thousands. They were scattered throughout the land they called Nod.

"Each succeeding generation knew less and less about the Creator. By the time Cain's great-great-great-grandson, Lamech, was born, there was only a distant memory of God. Instead, the people chose to worship creation itself – the sun, the moon, the mountains, and the rivers. Also, they had no knowledge of Eden. There was, however, still some knowledge of Cain's murderous act, though none could recall the details or the fact he had killed his brother. The only memory was that a law had been established long ago – that anyone who kills Cain is to be punished seven times. But no one could tell you why.

"Lamech married two women, both of whom were his cousins. One was named Adah and the other was Zillah. Adah gave birth to a baby named Jabal, who later grew up to be a herdsman and was the first generation to live under a tent. She also gave birth to a second son, Jubal, and he became the first musician, inventing the harp and the flute.

"Enoch, now you know where the idea of living under tents began and where the harp and flute originated. Though I never saw Cain again, nor any of his offspring, this earth is still just a large village and what one person does can affect the entire village!

"Through Zillah, Lamech fathered Tubal-cain. He became the first forger of metal, producing instruments of bronze and iron. As a result, the crude weaponry we used gave way to the more advanced – swords and knives with metal blades, and spears and arrows with metal tips."

I interrupted. "Is that where we got the idea to make metal blades and tips for our knives and weapons, Abot?"

"Yes, it is," he replied. "Remember, we're just a large village. Even their beliefs have influenced the rest of our people. Your family's beliefs are no longer much different from the beliefs of Cain's descendants. Sadly, because of our sinful nature, we all have the proclivity to turn away from our Creator."

Then he continued with his story. "One day, Lamech used one of those knives to kill a young man who attacked and wounded him. No one knew the young man's motives. The only statement to the rest of the tribe was one uttered by Lamech himself with great arrogance – *'If anyone who kills Cain is to be punished seven times, anyone who takes revenge against me will be punished seventy-seven times.'*[6]

No one seemed to recall that it was God who had established the former – and no one seemed to care when Lamech boisterously exclaimed the latter."

~

10

A PROMISED SAVIOR

~

It had been several weeks since I was able to sit with Abot and listen to his stories about our family history. It was harvest season for the wheat crop, and now that I was eleven, I was expected to do a greater share of the work in the fields.

One of the Creator's commands we still observed was resting on the seventh day of the week. In all honesty, I think it was less about being obedient to the Creator and more about our fathers realizing our bodies needed a day of rest.

I took advantage of one of those days to visit Abot in his tent. He picked right up with his story where he left off.

"I was 130 years of age when my son Seth was born, which meant over 120 years had passed between his birth and those of Cain, Awan, and Abel. With the large number of sons and daughters we welcomed into our family during those intervening years – as well as their succeeding generations – our extended family numbered well into the tens of thousands, just like Cain's.

"Though Matre gave birth to numerous sons between Abel and Seth, there was no mistaking that Seth was the one who looked most like me. The Creator told us Seth was a special gift from Him, which is why we named him Seth. His name means 'granted,' and as Matre said, '*God has granted me another son in place of Abel, the one Cain killed.*'[1]

"I knew he was the son to whom I would pass along the birthright that normally belongs to the oldest son. Though the Creator occasionally visited us after Cain murdered Abel, those visits had ceased by the time Seth was born.

"We looked back on those days with sadness and regret – and we still do. Our disobedience has caused so much pain and suffering. Our hearts break when a mother or baby dies during childbirth, when a child is attacked by a wild animal, or when someone tragically dies as the result of an accident. We know each of those deaths is a consequence of our sin.

"We remember the days when the wolf grazed with the lamb, the leopard lay down with the calf, the hyena played with the antelope, and the lion ate straw like the ox. We remember how we labored without growing weary, and how the plants grew abundantly without the restrictions of weeds, thistles, or thorns. And how the garden was a place filled with joy.

"Though we had spent time face to face with the Creator, we did not know how to worship Him now that He was no longer visible. We had talked with Him many times, but we did not know how to speak with Him when we could not see Him. So, our relationship suffered. Our sin created distance from our Creator, and that separation left unrepaired created even more distance. We knew that better than anyone!

"The day we disobeyed and ate the forbidden fruit, the Creator said to the serpent, '*From now on, you and the woman will be enemies, and your offspring and her offspring will be enemies. He will crush your head, and you will strike His heel.*'(2)

"It was clear to Matre and me that one of our offspring would one day crush the head of the evil one. Though the serpent would strike at His heel, the fatal blow would one day come to the evil one. He would be destroyed and the world would be put back to the way it had been before the evil one tempted Matre and we disobeyed God."

"When Seth was slightly older than you are now, I told him what I am telling you, Enoch. His eyes lit up when he asked, 'Father, does that mean that even at the moment of your disobedience, the Creator already had the remedy for your sin in mind? Is it possible that hope is not lost? The Creator has promised to send a Savior – One who will crush the head of the evil one. He will crush sin itself. The evil one did not win. He lost. And in the Creator's perfect timing, all will be realized!'

"Seth continued on excitedly. 'Father, our Savior will come from your offspring. And He has given me hope that our Savior will come from my offspring. He is the ultimate birthright you have passed to me. He may come during our lifetimes, or He may come after we have returned to dust. But He will come! Father, there is great reason for us to have hope! And we must learn how to talk with the Creator and walk with Him, even when we can't see Him or hear His voice!'

"From that moment, Seth continued to walk righteously before God. He seized the promise the Creator had given and walked with Him by faith – and he still does today.

"When he came of age, we arranged for him to marry his niece, Chava, whose name means life. Her great-grandfather is one of Seth's older brothers. The Lord blessed Seth and Chava with many sons and daughters.

With each son, Seth asked the Lord God if this was the one who would crush the evil one, but each time the Creator told him, 'No.'

"However, when Seth was 105, Chava gave birth to a son they named Enosh. The night he was born, the Lord told me through a dream that the Savior would come through my grandson Enosh's offspring. When I awoke the following morning, I went straightaway to Seth's camp to tell him the news.

"None of us has any idea how long we will need to wait, but we rejoiced together in knowing we were one generation closer to His arrival! When Seth shared the news with Chava, she asked me if it would be appropriate to dedicate Enosh to the Lord in light of the tremendous honor the Lord was bestowing upon him.

"I realized that day, at the age of 235 years, I had never dedicated any of my children, grandchildren, or other descendants to the Lord. Though it was not a practice I had followed, I knew Chava was correct and it was something we needed to do – and I needed to be the one to dedicate him!"

~

11

ONE CHILD IS DEDICATED, ANOTHER IS CONFUSED

~

"Enoch, since I had never dedicated my children to the Lord, I wasn't quite sure what to do," Abot continued. "Seth, Chava, Matre, and I gathered, together with the child, along the riverbank the next morning.

"As the sun appeared over the horizon, I took Enosh in my arms and raised him toward the heavens. I called out, 'Lord God Creator, You are the Maker of all life. Every good gift we have comes from You – including this little one. You have created him and entrusted him to us, just as you have all my children, their children, and their children's children – those who are gathered here and those who are scattered about.

"'Create within this child a heart to walk with You and seek You in all things. Protect him from the evil one when he attempts to turn him away from You. As he grows, make Enosh into a mighty man who seeks You above all else and walks uprightly.

"'Grant him the wisdom, strength, and faith to lead the family You one day grant him, as well as all of us, to do the same. Raise up the Seed through him You will one day use to defeat the evil one, once and for all, according to Your promise. Protect that Seed and allow that we might see Him in our lifetime for the salvation and forgiveness of all.'"

Abot went on to tell me he had three great regrets in life. He regretted his sin in the garden – because all other regrets stemmed from his disobedience to God. He regretted his failure to raise Cain in the instruction and fear of the Lord as well as failing to recognize the errant path Cain had chosen. And he regretted he had not dedicated each of his children to the Lord. He wondered aloud if things would have been different in Cain's life – and in the lives of the generations following him – if he had done so.

But Abot's face brightened as he went on to tell me more about his grandson. "During Enosh's childhood, we began to hear about musical instruments, including the harp and the flute, being fashioned by the estranged members of our family. From the day these instruments were introduced to our camp, Enosh demonstrated a gift for playing them – creating beautiful melodies that soothed the soul and lifted the spirit. It wasn't long before everyone in camp was either humming or whistling the melodies Enosh played.

"My grandson was only a few years older than you are now when he came to me with an idea. 'Grandfather,' he began, 'we all know every good and perfect gift we have has come from the Creator. I believe that is true of the melodies I play on the flute and harp. I believe He has given them to us so we might present them back to Him as a verbal offering. Those melodies, together with the words we might add, become an expression of our praise and worship to the Lord God Creator.

"'Grandfather, you have often told me about your walks with the Creator in the garden. You have told me about the closeness you felt to God during those days. That is how I feel when I play my melodies to Him and lift up my voice to Him. I can't see Him physically, but I can see Him in my mind's eye, and I can sense His presence as if He is standing right beside me.

"'I believe the Creator has given us music as a way for us to enjoy that same intimacy with Him that you once enjoyed with Him in the garden. I know music isn't the only way we can be close to God, but I believe He has given it to us as an additional way to worship Him.'"

Abot concluded his story about Enosh by saying, "I don't believe the descendants of Cain realized the Creator's purpose for the gift of music, but He has given it to us through them, nonetheless. It is a reminder that God works His will through all things – even when we don't realize it!"

As I returned home that afternoon, I reflected on all the stories Abot had told me over the past several weeks. I thought they were interesting, and I valued the time I spent with him – but I questioned the relevance of his stories to my life.

"Enoch, where have you been all day?" my father asked when I got home.

After I explained, he asked, "What do you think of Abot's stories?"

"I'm not sure what to think," I replied. "I know he believes them to be true – and in some ways, I want them to be true. But I am struggling to believe in a God who would allow His creation to disobey Him and then punish them for doing so. If He is truly God, couldn't He have stopped them from disobeying Him?"

"That is a very good question, my son. There is no doubt they are wonderful stories crafted by Abot to explain the events of his life. But Abot is very old, and I sometimes wonder how much of his story is real and how much is imagined," my father said. "You must come to that decision on your own as well – and you have plenty of time to decide."

12

A DARE AND A SNAKE

~

As the years passed, my brother Shep and I became fearless explorers. Our favorite spot was the hills and mountains on the east side of the river. We liked to climb to the highest peak and look out over the land. From there we could see across the western side of the valley all the way to the Euphrates River. It was a breathtaking sight.

The western face of the highest peak was a sheer drop of approximately 200 feet to a gradual slope. We normally hiked along the eastern path leading to the peak. But for some time now, Shep and I had been talking about climbing up the rocky face. After all, he and I were now fifteen and sixteen, respectively. We had often heard our older brothers bragging about climbing it. It almost seemed to be a rite of passage.

Whenever our mother heard any of us talking about it, she always forbade us from doing so. "I do not want you risking your lives over something that frivolous," she said on more than one occasion. But all of us boys just smiled and nodded. Sometimes our father would also add a halfhearted reprimand, but when our mother turned away, he would give us a wink.

Working in the fields each day kept Shep and me in pretty good physical shape. We also enjoyed a healthy brotherly competition. One day, we decided it was time for us to take on the rocky climb, and our conversation quickly turned into a challenge. I'm not sure who dared whom first, but it didn't take long before our minds were made up.

Since I was the older brother, I began my climb first. I was grateful to find there were plenty of cracks, lumps, and rough edges to provide hand and toe holds – just as our older brothers had said there would be. Once I had made it halfway to the top, Shep began his climb.

Periodically, I looked down to make certain my brother was all right. I eventually made it to the peak and pulled myself up onto the overlook. I then started watching my brother and shouting words of encouragement.

The last fifteen feet of the climb were actually the easiest. The angle was less severe and the ledges in the face were wider. Once Shep made it that far, we both began to celebrate our accomplishment. The anxiety we had stoically kept to ourselves was now behind us. We began to laugh and rehearse the words we were going to say to our older brothers later that night.

As Shep neared the overlook, he reached to take hold of the next ledge above him. Just then, a snake neither of us had seen struck and embedded its fangs in Shep's hand. He cried out in pain, but the greater challenge came from the fact that the snake had startled him. He lost his grip on the ledge and his one foot slipped off his toe hold. Though I attempted to grasp his hand, he was just beyond my reach. I watched in horror as my brother began free falling to the ground. He tried to grab a hand hold but failed.

His body hit the ground with a loud crack, immediately followed by an even louder thud as his head hit a rock.

"Shep!" I screamed at him over and over, willing him to respond. I knew the fastest way down was the path on the backside of the peak, so I took off running as fast as I could. It still took me five minutes to reach my brother.

As soon as I saw Shep's crumpled body up close, I knew he was dead. Ironically, the snake still had hold of Shep's hand and was lying lifeless beneath my brother's body, crushed by his weight as he landed on top of the snake with full force. For a moment, Abot's words about the head of the snake being crushed by his offspring echoed in my mind.

As I stood there, the magnitude of what had just happened crashed over me. My brother was dead . . . because of a meaningless dare. Sure, his fall had been an accident, and the dare had been mutual, but I still felt responsible. I dreaded facing my mother with the news. But more than anything, I grieved over losing my brother and my best friend. A life that should have lasted for centuries was snuffed out after fifteen short years.

Abot's story about Cain came to mind. I wondered if Cain had grieved for his younger brother, Abel. In Cain's case, it hadn't been an accident; it had been at his own hand. But had he ever felt any grief? I couldn't imagine what my life would be now without Shep, my closest confidant. Surely Cain must have felt something.

All of these thoughts were colliding in my mind – grief without comfort, questions without answers, and pain without relief. Suddenly, I cried out, "God of Abot! Where were You when the snake bit Shep's hand? Where were You when he fell to his death?

"Where were You when the snake convinced Matre and Abot to disobey You? Where were You when they fell from the paradise of that garden into this thorny and difficult world? Couldn't You have saved them? Couldn't You have saved Shep? Or is Your goodness just a wonderful story Abot made up? I think I will place my faith in the river god. At least I know where he is!"

I found some branches and created a stretcher to carry my brother's body back home. The heaviness of the journey was overwhelming – not from the weight of my brother, but from the weight of my grief.

13

WALKS THROUGH THE WOODS

~

My life wasn't the same after that day. Whenever I closed my eyes, I saw Shep's frightened expression as he struggled to grasp my outstretched hand. I blamed myself for his death, and though they never said it out loud, I believe my parents blamed me as well. There was a hole in my heart no one else would ever be able to fill.

I did not return to those hills; in fact, I stopped exploring east of the river altogether. I tried to compensate by spending more time working in the fields. I rationalized that I needed to make up for the fact there was one less worker now. I also discovered that if I kept busy, it distracted me from thinking about Shep.

Though Abot and Matre still lived nearby, I no longer visited them. Somehow the memory of Abot's stories made the pain of Shep's death even worse. Plus, I was convinced their God had been unable to prevent my brother's death. Either He did not have the power – or He just didn't care.

I became a loner. When I wasn't working, I frequently went for long solitary walks through the woods. During one of my meanderings, I encountered a girl named Dayana who told me she was lost. I didn't know her well but had occasionally seen her in the village. She was unsure how to get back home and asked if I would help her.

"I'm not headed home just yet, and I really don't want to talk right now," I replied. "But if you are agreeable to walking along with me in silence, our path will eventually lead back to your home."

She agreed and never once broke the silence. When we arrived back at her home, she told me she had enjoyed our walk and asked if we could do it again. To my own surprise, I agreed.

That became the first of many silent walks we took together. After a while, I found myself enjoying having a silent walking companion. Eventually, we even started to talk during those walks. She wasn't a chatterbox like most girls I knew, and I soon learned that when she spoke, it was always with purpose.

We discovered we were distant cousins with the same great-grandfather. I also found out she knew about Shep's death, as did most of the village. But, to her credit, she never asked me any questions about that day; rather, she allowed me to tell her what happened – over time, at my own pace.

After I had finished telling her the entire story during one of our walks, she looked into my eyes and said, "Enoch, Shep's death was a tragic accident, but it wasn't your fault. He wouldn't want you to live out the rest of your life believing you were responsible for his death. You both chose to climb that mountain. You both knew it was dangerous, but Shep chose to take the risk just like you did."

My parents and family had told me the same thing, but for almost four years I had refused to believe them . . . until that moment. Somehow, Dayana penetrated the walls I had built around my heart. I accepted her words, and the grief that had been dammed up for all those years suddenly came spilling out.

I dropped to my knees and began to weep. I had never shed a tear over Shep in front of anyone else. But somehow, I felt safe to cry in front of Dayana. She took my hands in hers, but she didn't say a word. She permitted me to be vulnerable in the comfort of her silence.

I would like to say my heart opened up to my parents and the rest of my family after that day – but it did not. I still felt like they blamed me for Shep's death. But I did allow Dayana in, and she has owned a place in my heart ever since.

Two years later, we became husband and wife. Abot, Matre, and all our family joined in our marriage celebration. That night as we all sat around the fire, Abot and Matre told us about their early days in Eden. "Toward the end of each day," Abot began, "the Creator would often invite us to join Him for a walk around the garden. Each time, He took us to a place in the garden we had never seen before, and we marveled at its beauty. The Creator explained every detail – why He had chosen each shape, each color, and each design.

"He told us that nothing had been left to chance. He designed and created each and every detail. And He reminded us that at the end of each day of creation, He had seen that everything was good and perfect."

We all listened respectfully to Abot, though none of us truly believed in the Creator. By this time, everyone viewed his stories as fascinating folklore. Dayana and I did agree about the beauty his stories described. We had seen that same beauty ourselves during our many frequent walks – even if we weren't in Eden.

Abot challenged us all, just as he always did, to turn our hearts back to the Creator. "Heed my words of truth! Do not worship those things He created, worship Him – the only One who is worthy of worship!" he declared. But like always, his impassioned plea fell on deaf ears and hardened hearts.

One year later, my oldest son, Aviv, was born. His name means "the beginning of spring." Since he was to be our firstborn of many to come, we thought it was an appropriate name. As the years passed, Dayana and I had many more sons and daughters. As our family grew, we had less time for our evening strolls through the woods. We missed those times together.

14

THE SONS OF CAIN

~

As the descendants of Adam continued to multiply, it was necessary for families and tribes to migrate to distant regions to find fertile land on which to settle and grow their food. Inevitably, that caused increased conflict as tribes began to settle in regions already claimed by other tribes.

We were hearing reports that large bands of robbers from the east, descendants of Cain, were attacking villages down river from us where Seth's descendants lived. Cain's people intended to wrestle control of the land by driving away the current occupants – through intimidation or death, whichever they deemed necessary.

So far, our village had been left alone. We weren't certain if they were avoiding us out of respect for Abot and Matre living here, or they just hadn't made their way to us yet. Regardless, we knew we could not sit idly by as our cousins were being attacked. We discovered the marauders were under the leadership of Obal, the tenth generation from Adam and the great grandson of Tubal-cain.

My father assembled our entire family and announced, "We must take up arms and help our extended family defend their villages against these bandits. Some of our men will remain here to defend our village, while the rest will go to aid the other villages."

Abot stood up and declared, "I will pray that the Creator goes before you and gives you victory over the evil intentions of the sons of Cain. I know you are farmers and not fighting men, but Jehovah God will fight for you!"

As we studied how Obal had defeated the villages, there was no question his planned attacks were strategic. Though the villages were each surrounded by protective walls, they obviously had not provided a good defense. We learned that Obal frequently led his attacks at first light while the village was still sleeping. The villagers would wake up disoriented and ill-prepared. We realized if we were going to defeat Obal, we would need to catch him off guard.

He would be expecting a frontal assault at his camp, so our best option was to surprise him when he was preparing to attack. Based on his attack pattern, we knew his next target was one of three villages. So, we needed to be prepared to launch counterattacks in those places.

My father divided our fighting force into thirds and chose two of my older brothers and me to each lead one of those divisions. I was given the responsibility of defending the village of Larak, named for one of Seth's grandsons. Jobab was the leader of the village. He and his sons and grandsons were brave men with an unbendable resolve to defend their village at all costs.

Jobab and I agreed on a strategy to defeat Obal if he attacked. After the sun set, we positioned our best archers at the most strategic vantage points in the tree line outside the village gate and on top of the village walls. I instructed them to remain out of sight and not release their arrows until they heard my signal.

At the same time, we positioned half of the remaining men with clubs and spears in the brush scattered throughout the forest; the rest of the men were stationed behind the city gate. They, too, were to stay hidden until they heard my signal.

Now came the hardest part – we needed to be alert and silent throughout the night to watch for Obal and his men. Our men posted at the two other villages saw nothing but the morning sun shining on an empty plain. But my men were rewarded with the arrival of Obal and his men walking right into our trap.

They stealthily approached the city, assuming the village was unprepared for their arrival. On my signal, our archers' arrows rained down on the attacking force from behind and above. Obal's men were out in the open and had nowhere to hide. They hastily retreated as our men behind the gate and in the brush assaulted them with spears and clubs.

Our men stood firm and fought bravely, and the fight was over in short order. Obal suffered an overwhelming defeat that day. Though I was grateful for our victory, I couldn't ignore the fact that we were family fighting family. Just as Cain had killed his brother, cousin was turned against cousin. And I feared this would not be the last time family blood was spilled.

I thought about what Abot said before we left our village to fight this battle. Had the Creator truly fought for us? All of Obal's men had died in the battle – but not one of our men perished! Jobab led his people to offer sacrifices to the sun god for his help in our victory. I, however, attributed the victory to our well-executed strategy.

In the days that followed, we remained watchful, doubting that the sons of Cain would halt their efforts because of one defeat. However, they made no further advances. It would be years before I discovered what caused their full retreat. Just as it would be years before I would truly understand what happened that day. But one thing I knew with certainty – the sun god had nothing to do with it!

15

AND THEN I WALKED WITH GOD

When I was sixty-five years old, Dayana announced that we were expecting another child. The births of our last three children had taken a toll on her physically, so I was concerned for her welfare.

From the first day we met, I learned that Dayana's eyes were the window to her soul. I could often tell what she was thinking by just looking into her eyes. And they were telling me she was weak and worried.

As time for the baby's arrival approached, so did the time for the first harvest of the year – which meant presenting our harvest offering to the river god. I had always asked the river god for a good yield, as well as health and prosperity. This time I decided I would ask him for strength and health for Dayana as she delivered our child. I made sure our offering was the absolute best of the best. I wanted the river god to be so pleased with me that he would not hesitate to grant my request.

Three days after I presented the offering, Dayana went into labor. I sent word to two women in our camp who were going to assist with the birth. After a short while, one of the women came to me and whispered, "Your wife does not look good. I fear she will not survive this birth."

"Oh yes, she will!" I replied. "I presented an excellent offering to the river god, and I am certain he will answer my request."

"I fear he will not," she answered, before returning to my wife.

At that moment, Abot and Matre arrived at our tent. "Enoch," Abot said, "we hear that your wife is about to give birth. We have come to extend our congratulations to you both!"

"We thank you for your good wishes," I replied, "but the baby has not yet arrived. And the midwives fear Dayana is not strong enough to deliver the child."

Matre hurriedly left to go to my wife. Abot motioned for me to sit down as he said, "I will pray with you to the Creator that He will give Dayana the strength to endure the pain and suffering of childbirth."

But before he could pray, Matre returned to tell us, "Dayana is at death's door. There is nothing any of us can do. We must pray that the Lord God Creator will heal her and strengthen her so she and the child might live."

"I prayed to the river god," I cried out, "but he did not answer me! If your God, the Creator, will have mercy on us and answer our prayer, I will turn to Him and follow Him alone for the rest of my days!"

All three of us knelt, and Abot began to pray. When he finished, I began. "Creator, I do not know You the way Abot does. I have denied Your existence most of my life. I have looked elsewhere to find You. I have looked to Your creation and denied Your power. I have accepted lies and denied Your truth. Forgive me, Oh God, for my sins. Forgive me for my faithlessness. I do not deserve Your mercy, but still I ask You to extend it. Today I turn to walk with You. Heal my wife and allow her and my child to live . . ."

Just then my prayer was interrupted by the sound of a baby's cry! Matre quickly went to check on Dayana. I continued to pray to the Creator while she was gone. The next sound I heard was not a baby's cry, it was the voice of the Creator – not audibly – but in my spirit saying, "Enoch, I have heard your cry and I have answered your prayer. Your wife lives and so does your child. Your child will be a sign to you and all of the people.

"There is a judgment coming to all of the people because of their wickedness and sinfulness. The day is coming when I will destroy every living thing. But I will hold off that judgment for as long as this child lives. He is my gift to you and Dayana, and the years of his life will be a gift to those who choose to follow Me. You will be My prophet and deliver My message of salvation to the people."

Just then Matre returned and told me to go see my wife. As I turned the corner, I saw my wife sitting up holding our baby. Dayana looked at me and smiled. The weakness I had seen earlier had been replaced with the joy and strength she usually exhibited. Gone was any sign of illness. Her health and strength had fully returned.

She turned our son's face toward me and said, "Enoch, meet your newest son! What should we call him?"

"His name will be Methuselah," I answered, "which means 'his death will send.' The Creator has told me our son will live a long life, but the judgment of God will be ushered in on the day of his death. His life will be a sign that the Creator has extended His mercy, but He will not withhold His judgment forever."

That was the day that changed my life. The Creator, by His mercy, spared my wife's life. He gave us many more years together, and together Dayana and I worshiped Him. He gave us a son – a son with a promise – for us and for all mankind. As wonderful as all of those precious gifts were to me that day, He gave me one more gift – one that was even greater. He gave me the gift of His presence. He granted me the privilege of walking with Him, just as Abot had once walked with Him. He granted me the gift of knowing Him intimately and speaking His truth. My life would never be the same!

~

16

A STILL, SMALL VOICE

When I told Dayana how I had prayed to the Creator and how He had answered my prayer, she, too, asked Him to forgive her sins. There was so much we had to learn and understand about Him and He patiently taught us. I also sought forgiveness from Abot and Matre for the disrespect I had shown them. They became a great encouragement to Dayana and me in our walk with God.

One of the greatest sorrows in my life is the fact that most of my older children did not turn to God. The sins and lies I lived out during my younger years greatly influenced them. They refused to accept the truth of a loving Creator who desired for them to have a relationship with Him. They blamed Him for all the evil in the world and rejected my pleas for them to repent. The Lord God had called me to be His prophet, but even my own children were refusing to heed the words of truth He was giving me to declare.

In the days immediately following Methuselah's birth, the Lord invited me to go on long walks with Him. He directed where He would have me go as we spoke. One day He invited me to cross the river and walk with Him through the land surrounding the mountain where Shep had died. I vehemently shook my head and told Him, "I can't go there!"

"Enoch, there are many places I will lead you as you walk with Me," the Creator said. "You must trust Me and know that I will never leave you nor forsake you. Some of the places I lead will be difficult for you. Some will involve giants from your past that I will lead you to conquer like this mountain. Trust Me no matter what it is. I will always have a purpose in it all!"

God was not only teaching Dayana and me, He was also teaching Methuselah even though he was just a lad. When Methuselah was six years old, he asked me, "Father, I hear you carrying on conversations with God, but the only one I ever hear is you. I can't see God or hear Him speaking back to you. Can you see or hear Him?"

"I don't always see Him with my eyes," I answered, "but I sense His presence, just as surely as I know you are right here with me."

"But, Father," he replied, "do you hear His voice?"

"He speaks to me in a still, small voice," I said. "I don't hear Him with my ears. I hear Him with my heart, and my spirit bears witness to all that He tells me."

"Have you ever seen Him with your eyes, Father?" Methuselah asked.

I nodded as I answered him, "Yes, on occasion He comes to me in person and invites me to walk with Him in the gardens like He once did with Abot."

My heart leapt for joy when he asked, "Father, can I join you when you go for walks with God?"

"That is up to the Creator," I replied. "He alone chooses how we enter into His presence. It's not because of who our family is, or even what we have done. He only chooses those who ask for His forgiveness and honestly seek Him and acknowledge who He is by faith. That is called living righteously, and though many may try to convince others through their actions that they are righteous, the Creator sees our hearts. He alone knows whose heart is truly turned toward Him."

"I want my heart to be truly turned toward Him," Methuselah declared with all the sincerity a little boy could muster.

"I know you do," I said. "And I pray that will always be the case. God has promised me you will be saved from the judgment that will one day come to this earth. Your death will be a signal that the time of judgment has come. I fear the days will become even more evil as that day approaches. I have asked the Creator to help you walk righteously before Him in the midst of that evil."

Our conversation was interrupted as we returned to the village. "We will continue this conversation another day," I told him. "Continue to seek Him and honor Him with all of your heart."

As the years passed, Methuselah developed an interest in carving wood. One day, while he was walking through the woods, he came upon a thick branch lying on the ground. As he stared at it, he began to imagine it was a panther crouched low to the ground and hunting for prey.

He picked up the branch and began to break off the portions of wood that were not part of his mental picture. Soon he realized he needed to use an instrument of some kind to create more delicate lines in the wood. He pulled out the small knife I had recently made for Him.

He sat down and began to carve. The more he carved, the more the piece of wood began to look like the panther in his mind. When he arrived home, he showed me what he had made. The carving was beautiful. I was amazed at the workmanship he demonstrated on his first effort at carving. I told him that clearly God had given him a gift to reflect the magnificence of creation through his woodwork.

But I was even more proud when he said, "The Creator told me in His still, small voice that carving is a lot like what He does in each of our lives. He has an image in His mind of what He intends for each of us to look like as we follow Him. He is patiently removing the large chunks and the small pieces from our lives that don't align with that image.

"It often hurts when He removes the larger chunks – and sometimes there is pain when He takes away the smaller pieces. But we need to trust that He knows what He is doing. He knows the image He is conforming us into!"

My son was becoming my teacher!

~

17

THE SERPENT'S BITE

~

As the years went by, Methuselah continued to practice and fine tune his wood-carving skills. He carved so many animals he could no longer think of one he had not chiseled. He asked Abot to describe more animals to him. Soon, many of the villagers were asking him to carve a bird or an animal for them. It was becoming a profitable skill.

In his late teens, Methuselah's eye was drawn to a girl named Mira, who was about his age and lived in our village. They began to take long walks together through the woods. One late afternoon as they were walking, Methuselah noticed a large, uniquely shaped tree branch on the ground. It was a size and shape he knew would produce a beautiful carving. As he reached down to pick it up, a snake appeared from the back side of it and lunged at his hand. It embedded its fangs deep into his flesh and held fast. Methuselah reached down with his other hand, picked up the piece of wood, and struck the snake. It released its hold and fell to the ground. Methuselah clubbed it to death with the large branch.

The area surrounding the two puncture wounds in his hand quickly began to turn red. He and Mira knew from the snake's markings that the bite was poisonous. They also knew a bite like this often leads to death – and there is no known cure.

Methuselah had the presence of mind to turn to his source of hope. He called out to the Creator, "Lord God, the venom from this snake is one of the consequences of the deceitful actions of the serpent in the Garden of Eden. But just as You were able to cause that serpent and all that would follow him to slither on the ground, You are able to remove the poisonous effects of this one's venom. You have promised that I will live a long and fruitful life – and I trust You for the fulfillment of that promise."

As Mira and Methuselah watched, the redness on his hand began to disappear. The pain subsided, and in a few moments the puncture wounds closed. The only evidence he had been bitten was the dead snake on the ground. The Creator had heard his prayer and healed him!

Methuselah brought the dead snake back to camp as evidence of what had just taken place. He intended for everyone in the village to hear the news of what the Creator had done. No one would be able to deny His power! "Our God is faithful!" he exclaimed to all who listened.

I sent word to Abot since I knew he would want to hear what the Lord God Creator had done. Though he was now 707 years old, Abot still had the strength of his younger days, and his resolve to honor the Creator in all things had not diminished. He joined his voice in praise over the goodness of God to my son.

"Just as the Lord God Creator promised," Abot said, "the serpent's head has again been crushed! Praise be to the One who is God over all. Though the evil one attempted to destroy this one who has been given as a reminder of God's mercy and grace, the Creator's might and power have proven that His promises will always be fulfilled. The evil one is a defeated foe!"

"But Abot," Methuselah asked, "how did the evil one ever come to be?"

"He was the most beautiful of God's creations," Abot replied. "He was created by God as a guardian cherub named Lucifer. He was *the signet of perfection, full of wisdom, and perfect in beauty.*(1) He was appointed to be the guardian over the Garden of Eden. But he rebelled against God. He was no longer content to be the most beautiful and most powerful created being; rather, he wanted to be God. He did not want to worship God, he wanted to be worshiped.

"That's why he came to Matre that day. He decided that if he could get God's creation to turn away from our Creator, he would prove himself to be greater than the Creator – he would be in the position of God. But the fact is, no matter how much he may want to be God, he never will be! He is a created being who will be judged and punished for his evil.

"The Creator cast him down from heaven and promised that He will send One who will ultimately defeat the evil one and redeem us from our sins. He will then reign over the earth and cast the evil one and those who have followed him into eternal damnation. And that Savior will come through our offspring. He will be born from my ancestral line. He will be born from your ancestral line, Methuselah. That's why he sought to kill you and made a feeble attempt to prevent God from accomplishing His purpose through your life. But He is a defeated foe, just like this dead snake lying on the ground!"

Though the evil one's attempt to destroy my son had been defeated, we knew he was still at work to corrupt the descendants of Adam. Word had already reached us that other angelic beings who had chosen to follow the evil one now walked the earth. They had first arrived in the land called Nod – the land inhabited by the descendants of Cain. There they saw the beautiful women of the human race and took those they chose to be their wives.

I declared to all who were gathered, "The Creator has told me that the evil one continues to prowl the earth in his effort to accomplish his evil intent. He has apparently decided that if the Savior will be a descendant of Abot, he will attempt to foil the plan by corrupting the entire human race – not only through our sin nature, but also through the intermarriage of his demonic angels with the daughters of Adam and Eve.

"The Creator told me the evil one believes that if he infects the entire human race through his demonic beings, there will be no line through which the Savior can be born. But, as always, the evil one has underestimated the Sovereign and Almighty God! His purpose and plan will not be thwarted – that which He has put in motion will be accomplished!"

18

THE SONS OF GOD

~

In the days that followed, we heard additional reports of the evil deeds of the fallen angels. The Creator had shown me that the greatest weapon wielded by the evil one was the weapon of deceit. Sadly, he had used that weapon quite effectively to lead Abot and Matre astray in the garden, and he had continued to use it successfully ever since.

But his efforts were not limited solely to the descendants of Adam here on earth; he employed that same weapon to enlist the complicity of the sons of God – the angels in heaven. While they were still yet in heaven, before the Lord God cast them out, the evil one craftily deceived many of the angels with promises of personal power and gain. Angels cannot see into the future any more than the evil one can, so many of them had blindly fallen prey to his wiles.

As time passed, the evil one pointed out the beauty of the growing number of daughters of Cain and introduced the seed of lustful desire and thoughts into their hearts. In heaven the angels had never engaged in sexual relations, nor had they ever had any desire. The thought of doing so went against everything they had known since the Lord God had created them. Though they were fallen angels, they still had some understanding of right and wrong.

But the evil one would not be put off by their apprehension. He decided to raise up an accomplice from among their number with the promise of increased power in the evil one's kingdom on earth. The evil one established a fallen angel named Semjaza as a leader over them all and instructed him on how to lead the others to act on their lustful desires.

Semjaza stood before the other fallen angels and said, "Come, let us choose wives from among the children of men who will bear children unto us, as our master, Lucifer, has instructed us to do. I fear you will not agree to do what he has asked, and I alone will have to pay the penalty for this great sin. But I question if there is truly a penalty, or rather is it a prize we have been denied? The Creator has given this pleasure to men; why should it not also be ours?"(1)

After a moment's hesitation, the multitude answered back in unison, "Let us all swear an oath, and bind ourselves by a mutual curse not to abandon this plan but to do this thing."(1) They bound themselves with full knowledge of their sin and chose to take wives from the daughters of men.

They taught their wives charms, enhancements, and how to practice other forms of divination. The evil that had begun among men in the Garden of Eden was now being escalated beyond description. And in the midst of this evil, they bore a race of giants who, in turn, furthered the evil practices introduced by their progenitors.

However, the depravity did not stop there. When the daughters of men could no longer satisfy their desires and the sons of men could no longer sustain them, the giants turned against them and began to devour mankind. Their deviant practices soon involved all manner of evil against all living things. But still their thirst for evil would not be quenched. They began to devour one another's flesh and drink the blood.

The Lord looked down at the wickedness that now extended throughout His creation and was sorry He had ever made any of it – the created beings that had fallen from heaven and mankind who now occupied the earth.

One day as I was walking with Him, He declared, *"I will completely wipe out this human race that I have created. Yes, and I will destroy all the animals and birds, too. I am sorry I ever made them!"*[(2)]

My heart was broken over His anguish, and I suddenly found myself thinking, "Lord, will you destroy both the innocent and guilty alike?" But I didn't merely think those words, I suddenly realized I had spoken them out loud!

I had never before questioned God about anything He said He was going to do. I did not know how He would react. After all, who am I to question the Sovereign and Almighty God? Where was I when He created the world? Who am I to question the One who spoke the sky, the land, and the seas into existence? How could I even pretend to question the One who created the very beings that He now determined He would need to destroy?

Besides, are any of us truly innocent? We have all come from the seed of Adam. We are all sinners. Why should we presume that the Creator spare any of us?

But then I heard Him speak. "I will spare those who are righteous from the wrath of My judgment," He said. "I will remove them from this earth before I unleash my judgment.

"I will be gracious and faithful to them, just as I have been to you. On the day you led your men to attack the forces of Obal at Larkin, I was there with you. Even though you denied My existence and My power, I was gracious to you and spared the lives of all of your men. How much more will I be faithful to those who turn their hearts to Me!

"And even in the midst of My judgment, I will spare one man and his family from death. He will be a righteous man through whom I will replenish the earth as I intended."

"Lord, when will this be and who is this man?" I asked.

"It is for Me only to know the time. But I have given you a promise that your son Methuselah will not die until that day of judgment has arrived. And the one through whom I will replenish the earth will be of his seed – your seed, Enoch!

'Now, you must be about the work I have given you. You are not to invest your time worrying when I will bring judgment or how I will do so. Your work is to call those who will respond to repentance! Make haste, Enoch, for the day of judgment will come soon!"

19

SHARED JOY . . . AND SHARED SORROW

~

When I was 252 years old, Methuselah and Mira were blessed with a son they named Lamech, which means strong and vigorous. The Creator gave me three promises regarding my grandson: He would walk in righteousness before His God. He would be saved from the coming day of judgment. And the Savior whom God would one day send to earth would be born through Lamech's ancestral line.

The day Methuselah and Mira dedicated Lamech to the Lord, Dayana, Abot, Matre, and I stood by their sides. It was then the Lord gave me one more promise. He said Lamech would live a long life – and Methuselah would be there to walk beside him each and every day.

When Lamech was old enough to understand, his father and I told him of God's promise that the Savior of the world would come from his lineage. I was proud of his understanding and spiritual maturity when he asked, "Why am I in that line? What have I done – or what could I ever do – that is so outstanding I would be considered worthy to be part of God's eternal plan?"

"You have done nothing to earn God's favor," I said. "It is God's mercy and grace extended to you. You do not walk with God out of privilege, you walk with Him by faith!"

From an early age, Lamech demonstrated carpentry skills, just like his father. Until my son's generation, each of us had primarily been farmers who also did everything else needed to provide for our families. But in more recent years, many had begun taking on a trade using their unique talent and skills.

People would then barter their trade for the goods or services provided by others. It became a more efficient way to glean what was needed, and everyone felt more fulfilled doing the work they enjoyed. Some of my sons and grandsons cultivated the land like my father had done, and others became capable hunters, pottery makers, tanners, weavers, and the like.

When Lamech turned eighteen, his parents arranged for him to marry a young woman named Shira who lived in our village. Her name means singing, and she truly brought music into our lives. God soon blessed them with a home full of children.

When I was 282 years old, our family experienced a difficult loss. We always knew the day would come, but that didn't make us any more prepared. Matre died at the age of 900. She was the matriarch of us all. Her family numbered more than anyone could count. Some said it was in the billions; I don't know about that, but it was definitely a lot!

Obviously, the one most affected by her death was Abot. She was bone of his bone and flesh of his flesh. They had been husband and wife for every day of their lives. They alone shared the memory of Eden. They alone had seen the sun rise and set every day since the beginning.

None of us could imagine their shared joys – or their shared sorrows. We would never know the weight they carried because they ushered sin into the world. None of us would ever enjoy the simplicity of life unburdened by the knowledge of good and evil. And we would never experience walking in fellowship with God without any element of sin to separate us.

Death is a reminder of sin. The Creator never intended for us to experience physical death. Our bodies were never intended to grow old. The ages of all of our patriarchs, including this generation, were a constant reminder of God's original intention. But recently God had told me, *"My Spirit will no longer put up with humans for such a long time, for they are mortal flesh. In the future they will live no more than 120 years."*[1]

Today, 120 years is considered young, but one day soon that age will be considered very old, which means the aging process we all go through will accelerate. Even though God said it, it was still hard for me to imagine at the age of 282 what that would be like.

Though we sent out word to many other villages and cities about Matre's death, few of her descendants knew of her passing, and even fewer grieved her death. Many probably didn't even know her name.

Members of my family – including Seth and Chava, together with their son, Enosh, and his wife – traveled to our village to pay their respects. Seth was now 770 and Enosh was 665, so travel was difficult for them. None of Matre's other sons came, and we didn't think any of them were walking righteously before God. Sadly, that was a sorrow most of us as parents could understand.

Soon after the mourning period was over, I suggested to Abot that he move in with Lamech and Shira. It would be good for him to be surrounded by their happy family, and it would be an honor and privilege for them to care for him.

I knew this was another reminder that the day of judgment was coming soon.

20

THE SECOND ADAM

~

In the days that followed, the Lord took me to a place I had never been before. He said it would one day be called Horeb – the mountain of God. As I knelt before Him, He allowed me to see a vision: the Creator took me into the heavens where I saw One whose countenance was that of a Man with a kind face.

I asked one of the heavenly hosts standing near to me who the Man was, and he replied, "This is the Promised One – the Son of Man – who is and was and forever will be. Yea, before the sun and the stars were created, His name was named. He shall be a staff to the righteous, light to the Gentiles, and the hope of those who are troubled of heart. All who dwell on earth shall one day fall down and worship Him with praise and blessing and celebration.[1]

"And on that day, the earth will give back that which has been entrusted to it, Sheol will give back that which it has received, and hell will give back that which it owes. For in those days, the Son of Man will arise, and He will choose the elect from among them for the day will have drawn nigh that they should be delivered.[1]

"And the Son of Man will in those days sit on the Creator's throne, and His mouth will pour forth all wisdom, counsel, and judgment. The earth will rejoice, the righteous will dwell upon it, and the elect will walk thereon."[1]

The Lord God Creator permitted me to see all the secrets of the heavens, how the kingdom is divided, and how the actions of men are weighed in the balance. I saw the mansions of the elect and the mansions of the heavenly hosts. My eyes saw all the sinners being cast away into the punishment they will be forced to endure forever.

Then I looked down and saw a deep valley with fire where the sinners were being cast. Beside the opening of the valley were iron chains of immeasurable weight. I asked the angel, "For whom are those chains being prepared?"[1]

He said to me, "These are being prepared to subdue the evil one and the angels who followed him just before they are cast into the abyss of complete condemnation. And their jaws will be covered with rough stones so they will not be able to utter another deceptive word. The angels of the Lord will take hold of them on that day and cast them into the burning furnace as their punishment for leading astray those who dwelt on the earth."[1]

When I awoke there on the mountain of Horeb, the Lord God Jehovah said to me, "Go and tell everyone what you have seen. Say unto them:

"Listen! The Lord is coming with countless thousands of His holy ones to execute judgment on the people of the world. He will convict every person of all the

ungodly things they have done and for all the insults that ungodly sinners have spoken against Him."[2]

In the blink of an eye, He delivered me to a hillside overlooking a city where I now stood alone. However, He left no doubt as to what I was to do and say:

"Hear, you men of old, and see, you that have come after, the words of the Holy One which I have been sent to declare . . ."

I then proceeded to proclaim everything God had permitted me to see.

When I was 308 years old, Abot died. He was 930 years of age. Though a few of his descendants would live longer than he did, none of them would ever experience what he had during his lifetime.

As I helped prepare his body for burial, I lingered a moment as I saw the scar God left when He removed the rib from which He formed Matre. As I saw his stomach, I was again reminded by the absence of a navel that Abot had never been inside a mother's womb. He had experienced things the rest of us would never know.

In his later years, Abot and I often talked about the privilege God had given both of us to walk with Him. Abot always looked sad when he said those words, because he knew his sin had cost him that privilege. But then he would smile as he looked at me and say, "Enoch, the Creator has given you the privilege of walking with Him as a friend walks with a friend. Do not ever do anything to lose that privilege. No relationship can ever replace it."

Abot had taught me more than any other man in my life. Of all of the millions – or billions – of his descendants still living, he chose to invest his life in mine. I could have been like so many and never really known him. But through his effort and by God's grace that wasn't the case. I would miss him greatly. But I knew better than most that I would see him again one day.

The first Adam would live again – because the One who would become known as the second Adam would one day come to earth to make that possible! And both Adams would share one important distinction – neither was created through the seed of an earthly father!

As word spread throughout cities and villages that Abot had died, the whole earth stopped to honor him and mourn his passing. A week of mourning was declared to grieve his death. For those few brief days, the righteous and unrighteous came together in a single purpose. It was said that those days of mourning were the first and last days that all people united since that fateful day in the Garden of Eden. And I knew it would not occur again until the day the Second Adam comes to judge and reign over all the earth.

~

21

WALKING THROUGH THE DIFFICULT DAYS

~

"Methuselah," I said, "call to me all of your sons. For the Word calls me, and the Spirit is poured out upon me, that I may show you and your children everything that shall befall you and the generations to come."[(1)]

When Methuselah's family had assembled, I declared, "Hear, you sons of Methuselah, all the words of your grandfather, and harken to my voice. I exhort you and say to you, beloved, love uprightness and walk therein. Do not be drawn away from uprightness by your deceitful hearts, and do not associate with those who are double-minded.[(2)]

"But walk in righteousness, my sons. It will guide you on right paths and lead you where you are to walk. Violence will increase on the earth and a great chastisement is coming soon. Yes, the earth will be cut off from its roots, and its whole structure will be destroyed. But you can yet escape that destruction. [(2)]

"In the days preceding the great chastisement, unrighteousness together with all of its deeds and violence will be on the increase, as will apostasy and transgression. Then the Holy Lord will pour out His wrath and chastisement to execute His judgment upon the earth.[2]

"The roots of unrighteousness and deceit will be destroyed. The idols of the heathen will be abandoned, their temples will be obliterated, and the unrighteous themselves will perish in judgment forever.[2]

"So now, harken unto me, my sons, and walk in the paths of righteousness. For all who walk in the paths of unrighteousness will perish in the judgment forever."[2]

But the only son of Methuselah who chose to walk in the path of integrity and honor was Lamech. Even Lamech's adult sons chose the paths of deception, trusting in their own riches and the false thinking of the world.

At the Creator's prompting, I continued to declare the warning of God's upcoming judgment to all men, but they responded much the same as the sons of Lamech. There was little question that only a few would follow the narrow path of righteousness leading up to the day God would cry out, "Enough!"

Dayana would often come to me and ask, "How much longer will the Creator delay in sending His judgment? Surely, He has extended mercy beyond all reason."

Each time I would reply, "He will delay His judgment until His perfect time has arrived. We cannot comprehend His ways. His grace and mercy are beyond anything we could ever understand. But let there be no doubt – the day of His judgment will arrive!"

God granted our family peace and safety despite the evil surrounding us. Though the people rejected their Creator, they felt some sense of respect for Abot and Matre.

We knew God was our protector, but our neighbors told us we would not be harmed because our family had cared for Abot and Matre in their final years. So, each day we walked through the fire of evil knowing God would keep even the clothes on our backs from being singed.

I have learned over the years that walking with God is rarely a serene, peaceful walk. It is a walk that requires faith and courage. He does not only lead me beside the still waters, but He also sometimes leads me through the raging fires and the howling winds. I have walked with Him to the highest peaks and surveyed His majesty, but I have also walked with Him to the lowest depths of anguish and death.

Knowing He was right by my side for every step is what has given me strength, comfort, and assurance. I have never needed to ask Him what step to take or where to go. I have learned if I keep my eyes on Him and remain by His side, He will always lead me to the exact spot He wants me to be – no matter how majestic, mundane, or terrifying.

Over the years, He has led me to confront murderers, sorcerers, and those who practice all manner of evil. He has led me to stand alone in the midst of evil doers who vehemently reject the message of repentance. But the most difficult place He has ever led me was to the bedside of my dying wife.

We had been married 342 years. I could barely remember a day when we were not together. We had walked with God hand in hand. We had encouraged one another when the journey was difficult, and we had celebrated with each other when the days were filled with overwhelming joy. I cried out to the Lord, just as I had done 295 years earlier.

"Lord, You answered my prayer even when I denied Your existence! You healed my wife and allowed her and my son to live. Would you do it again? Would you spare her life and permit us to live out our lives together? You know my frame! You know how much I depend on her. She is the helpmate You created for me. Spare her, Oh Lord!"

I felt His presence. I knew He was right there with me. His invitation to walk with Him all those years ago had also assured me He would always be with me. And this was one of those times.

I heard His reassuring voice as He said, "Enoch, it is time for her to die. She has completed her race, and she has finished well. I have more for you to do, which will not necessitate her being by your side. If you understood what that is, you would agree. But for now, you need to trust Me.

"Dayana is as much My child as you are. Believe it or not, I love her even more than you do. It is time for her to enter into her rest. It is time for you to let her go. You will see her again one day – and on that day there will be no more sadness and no more pain. In the meantime, trust Me to draw both of you close to Me."

I held the hands of my precious wife as our Creator permitted us one more treasured moment. Though her eyes had remained closed for several days, she opened them for one brief moment. As my eyes met hers, we said goodbye – not in words, but through our gaze . . . one I will hold in my heart until the day we again look upon one another.

~

22

DAYS OF MERCY AND GRACE

~

Two years after Dayana died, the Lord told me to go visit my ancestors, Seth (son of Adam) and Enosh (son of Seth). They were living in a village two days' journey downriver. I had last seen them fifty-four years earlier on the occasion of Abot's death. I didn't yet know why the Lord wanted us to visit them, but I knew He would show me in His perfect timing.

Seth and his wife, Chava, welcomed Methuselah, Lamech, and me with open arms, as did Enosh and his wife. The news of my warnings about God's coming judgment had reached their village. "Sadly," Seth told us, "most of our neighbors view your warnings as the rantings of a lunatic instead of a warning from the Almighty God. And they no longer listen to the melodies of worship that Enosh sings. Instead of being moved to repentance and worship, they mock the words – and worse, they mock the Lord God Creator.

"I count it a blessing that you three men are walking with God. Most of those here in our village are also my descendants, and my heart aches that they, like many others, have turned their backs on our Creator."

"Sadly, that is also true of my father (Jared) and my grandfather (Mahalalel), who are also your direct descendants," I said.

"And it is true of my son (Kenan), who is their immediate ancestor," Enosh replied.

"That means three of the men who stand between the three of us and the two of you generationally will enter into the judgment of God separated from Him if they continue to refuse to repent of their sins," I acknowledged.

"We must once more urge the three of them to turn from their wicked ways. I will summon them to come here for a gathering of their ancestral line from the second generation of Adam through the ninth," Seth declared. "They will not refuse an invitation for this once-in-a-lifetime gathering – a reunion of eight generations!"

He prepared messages and had them sent to the three men. By the end of the week all three had arrived in his village. The generations included:

Seth, aged 854,
Enosh, aged 749,
Kenan, aged 659,
Mahalalel, aged 589,
Jared, aged 524,
Me, aged 362,
Methuselah, aged 297, and
Lamech, aged 110.

"Sons, and sons of my sons," Seth began once we were all gathered, "we are the generations that followed our patriarch, Adam. We are the ancestral line through whom the One promised to Adam will one day come. We have been given the honor of bearing the seed of the One who will defeat the evil one deceiving our people.

"For this divine purpose, we should be men who walk righteously before God. And yet, some of you have chosen to pursue your own path and have disregarded the words of Adam. You have disregarded the one who knew better than any man the true cost of going your own way.

"You have heard Enoch deliver the warnings from our Creator. God has called him to be His prophet, bringing His message of the coming judgment to our wicked generations. And yet some of you have not heeded his warnings.

"What more do you men need? Your father, Adam, and one of your sons, Enoch, have both been used by God to call all people to repentance. You, who share their bloodline, should be the first to accept their words as truth. You men should be first among all men to walk righteously before our God and Creator.

"You men, above all others, have been blessed by God to be the bearers of His message. How can you obstinately turn your backs on Him and pursue your own evil ways? As your sole living patriarch, I beg you, as do Enosh and these three of your sons – Enoch, Methuselah, and Lamech. Repent of your wickedness, turn back to your Creator, and live righteously so you might escape the coming judgment. And urge your offspring to do the same."

I would like to tell you my great-grandfather, my grandfather and my father all repented that day and made the decision to walk honorably before God – but they did not. They all told Seth they would consider his words and my message of repentance and decide for themselves. I never saw a change in my father's or grandfather's actions, so I fear they did not. I do not know what my great-grandfather chose to do.

But Seth and I were obedient to what God directed us to do by giving our family members one more opportunity to repent. I never saw Seth, Enosh, or Kenan again, but I had a peace knowing I had done what God wanted me to do. He reminded me – that just like all people – they needed to decide for themselves. No one escapes the judgment of God because their parent or grandparent walked righteously with God. Each one must choose.

A few months later, God took me to a high peak on the mountains of Ararat. As I looked out over the expanse of land, God told me, "The days of mercy and grace I have extended to this evil generation are coming to an end. One day soon I will cover the earth with a flood that will destroy every living thing. Everything on earth will die. But I will raise up a remnant from your seed and keep him and his family safe from the flood waters in a boat I will direct him to build. They will bring a pair of every living animal and bird into the boat to keep them alive as well."(1)

"The one through whom I will do this has not yet been born. He will be the son of your grandson Lamech – and so the ancestral line that will one day lead to the birth of the Savior will be preserved. That which I have promised will be accomplished.

"Enoch, I will also keep my promise regarding Methuselah and Lamech. They will not experience that day of judgment. I will permit them to die peacefully before that day arrives. Just as I promised you and Dayana, Methuselah's death will usher in the flood waters.

"And Enoch, you will not experience those days either – because I have a different assignment for you!"

But He did not tell me what the assignment was.

23

AND THEN . . . HE TOOK ME

That brings me back to where I began telling you my story. Another year has passed. Today God led me to a distant place. He placed my feet on a hill that overlooked a city. But this city is unlike any other I have ever seen. He told me we were standing there on a future day, and the name of the city is Jerusalem.

He told me His Promised One had already come. But instead of being welcomed and embraced, He was despised and rejected. Most people had turned their backs on Him and looked the other way.

I cried out, "Lord, they sound just like the people of my day – rejecting You – and rejecting Your truth!"

"Yes, they too have been deceived by the evil one," He continued. "Not only did they reject Him, but they also crucified Him on a cross on this very hill."

His voice momentarily faltered as He continued. "They spat on Him, they persecuted Him, and they murdered Him as if He were a common criminal. But what they did not realize was that through His death on that cross, He took upon Himself the sins of them all. He offered Himself as a sinless and spotless sacrifice so that their sins – and your sins, Enoch – could be forgiven.

"But He did not remain in the grave. On the third day, He arose – conquering sin and death! My Son became the second Adam. Physical life was given through your ancestor, the first Adam. But eternal life – life freed from the bondage of sin – was given through My Son, the second Adam. The work of redemption is complete. All who have turned to Him by faith will live with Me forever.

"My final judgment is at hand. This judgment will not be a flood. It is the judgment that you have foretold through the words I have given you! And My Son, the second Adam, the One whom they crucified, will soon return as King and Judge over all. As we look down upon this city, His return is but moments away.

"But, in My mercy and grace, I extended one last invitation to the people to repent of their sins and turn by faith to My Son. I sent two prophets to be olive trees and lampstands to stand among them declaring the day of salvation and judgment. They remained on the earth bearing witness for 1,260 days – but then the evil one and all those who follow him put them to death.

"They celebrated what they perceived to be their victory – just as they celebrated the death of My Son. But just like My Son, after three-and-one-half days, the spirit of life returned to them![1] All this occurred in the city below. I have brought you here to see where those final days took place!"

"Lord, who are the two witnesses who were killed?" I asked.

"They are two prophets I selected even before I created the earth. They are men who have been My faithful witnesses, whom I created and redeemed for just this purpose. They are men who lived on this earth in a prior day as prophets of old. They are men who faithfully completed the assignments I gave them in their day. And they are men I took from this earth without their having to experience death.

"They did not experience death then, because they experienced death in this future time. Because *it is appointed for men to die once, and after that comes the judgment.*[2] And once the spirit of life returned to the two witnesses, I shouted from heaven, *'Come up here!'* And they rose to heaven in a cloud as their enemies watched!"[3]

For a moment, He paused and we stood in silence. I had come to recognize over the years that God not only entrusts us with His Word, He also entrusts us with His silence. I learned to resist the temptation to run ahead and try to fill the silence with my words or actions. Rather, He taught me to be still, and know that He is God. In His perfect timing, He will break the silence. And in His time, He did.

"Enoch," He said, "you are one of those witnesses. I created you, chose you, and empowered you for this assignment. Just as My Spirit has gone with you throughout your past days, I will go with you in the days yet to come. You completed all I planned for you to do in these past days. Now it is time for you to come with Me and prepare for the remainder of My assignment for you.

"Today you began the day in your home here on earth, but you will end it with Me in your new home in heaven."

I hesitated for a moment because I had one question for my Lord. But He who knows our every thought already knew what was on my mind.

"No," He said, "you cannot return to your home to say goodbye to your family. I know that is hard. That is why I allowed Dayana to die early, so she would not be left to continue on by herself. Your sons will continue in the paths I have set before them. And one day soon, you will be reunited with them all."

"Lord, what will they think has happened to me?" I asked. "Will they think I have been eaten by a wild animal, or killed and buried like Cain did to Abel?"

"No," my Lord replied, "they will know that you faithfully walked with Me, and on this day, I took you. I will give their spirits that assurance. I will remind them and all generations that follow, that you pleased Me – and that it is impossible to please Me without faith!"(4)

I looked down at the city of Jerusalem one more time before I turned my gaze back on my Lord. In the twinkling of an eye, I was no more . . . because my Creator took me! And, oh, what a sight I now behold!

~

SCRIPTURE BIBLIOGRAPHY

~

Much of the story line of this book is taken from the first six chapters of the Book of Genesis as recorded in Scripture. As explained in the preface, i also make references to The Book of Enoch, an apocryphal book.

Certain fictional events or depictions of those events have been added.

Some of the dialogue in this story are direct quotations from Scripture. Here are the specific references for those quotations:

Preface

(1) Genesis 5:21-22

(2) Jude 14

(3) Genesis 5:23

(4) 2 Kings 2:11

(5) Hebrews 9:27 (NASB)

(6) *The Book of Enoch*

[7] Jude 14-15

Chapter 1

[1] Adapted from Chapter 1 of *The Book of Enoch*

Chapter 2

[1] Genesis 1:28 (ESV)

[2] Genesis 3:17b-19a

Chapter 3

[1] Genesis 2:16-17

[2] Genesis 2:18

[3] Genesis 2:23

[4] Genesis 1:28-30

Chapter 4

[1] Genesis 3:1

[2] Genesis 3:2-3

[3] Genesis 3:4-5

[4] Genesis 3:9

[5] Genesis 3:10

[6] Genesis 3:11

[7] Genesis 3:12

[8] Genesis 3:13

[9] Genesis 3:13

Chapter 5

[1] Genesis 3:14-15

[2] Genesis 3:16

[3] Genesis 3:17-19

[4] Genesis 3:22

Chapter 6

[1] Genesis 4:1

Chapter 8

[1] Genesis 4:6-7

Chapter 9

[1] Genesis 4:9

[2] Genesis 4:9

[3] Genesis 4:10-12

[4] Genesis 4:13-14

[5] Genesis 4:15

[6] Genesis 4:24

Chapter 10

[1] Genesis 4:25

[2] Genesis 3:15

Chapter 17

[1] Ezekiel 28:12 (ESV)

Chapter 18

[1] Adapted from Section 1, Chapter 6 of *The Book of Enoch*

[2] Genesis 6:7

Chapter 19

[1] Genesis 6:3

Chapter 20

[1] Adapted from Section 2, Chapters 37, 41, 46, 47, 48, 51, 54 of *The Book of Enoch*

[2] Jude 14-15

Chapter 21

[1] Adapted from Section 3, Chapter 82 of *The Book of Enoch*

[2] Adapted from Section 5, Chapter 91 of *The Book of Enoch*

Chapter 22

[1] Adapted from Genesis 6:17-21 (spoken by God to Noah, not Enoch)

Chapter 23

[1] Revelation 11:3-11

[2] Hebrews 9:27 (NASB)

[3] Revelation 11:12

[4] Hebrews 11:5-6

References to *The Book of Enoch* are taken from *The Book of Enoch,* The Apocrypha and Pseudepigrapha of the Old Testament, edited by H. R. Charles Oxford, published by The Clarendon Press

~

LISTING OF CHARACTERS (ALPHABETICAL ORDER)

~

Many of the characters in this book are real people pulled directly from the pages of Scripture. i have not changed any details about a number of those individuals, except the addition of their interactions with the fictional characters. They are noted below as "UN" (unchanged).

In other instances, fictional details have been added to real people to provide backgrounds about their lives where Scripture is silent. The intent is that you understand these were real people, whose lives were full of the many details that fill our own lives. They are noted as "FB" (fictional background).

In some instances, we are never told the names of certain individuals in the Bible. In those instances, where i have given them a name as well as a fictional background, they are noted as "FN" (fictional name).

Lastly, a number of the characters are purely fictional, added to convey the fictional elements of these stories. They are noted as "FC" (fictional character).

Abel – second son of Adam & Eve (FB)
Adah – wife of Lamech (line of Cain), mother of Jabal & Jubal (UN)
Adam/ Abot – the first man, created by God, father of Cain, Awan, Abel & Seth (FB)
Aviv – eldest son of Enoch & Dayana (FC)
Awan – eldest daughter of Adam & Eve, wife of Cain (FC)
Cain – eldest son of Adam & Eve, husband of Awan (FB)
Chava – wife of Seth, mother of Enosh
Dayana – wife of Enoch, mother of Aviv & Methuselah (FC)
Enoch, son of Cain – eldest son of Cain & Awan (UN)
Enoch, son of Jared – son of Jared, husband of Dayana, father of Aviv & Methuselah, prophet of God (FB)
Enosh – son of Seth & Chava, father of Kenan (FB)
Eve/ Matre – the first woman, created by God, wife of Adam, mother of Cain, Awan, Abel & Seth (FB)
Jabal – son of Lamech & Adah (line of Cain) (UN)
Jared – son of Mahalalel, father of Enoch & Shep (FB)
Jobab – leader of fictional village of Larak (FC)
Jubal – son of Lamech & Adah (line of Cain) (UN)
Kenan – son of Enosh, father of Mahalalel (FB)
Lamech, son of Methuselah – son of Methuselah, husband of Shira, father of Noah (FB)
Lamech, son of Methushael – great-great-great-grandson of Cain & Awan (FB)
Mahalalel – son of Kenan, father of Jared (FB)
Methuselah – son of Enoch, husband of Mira, father of Lamech (FB)
Mira – wife of Methuselah, mother of Lamech (FC)
Obal – great-grandson of Tubal-cain (FC)
Semjaza – leader of fallen angels (named in the Book of Enoch) (FC)
Seth – son of Adam & Eve, inherited birthright, husband of Chava, father of Enosh (FB)
Shep – son of Jared, younger brother of Enoch (FC)
Shira – wife of Lamech, mother of Noah (FC)
The Creator – the Sovereign and Almighty God (UN)

The Promised One – Jesus Christ, the Son of God (UN)
Tubal-cain – son of Lamech & Zillah (the line of Cain) (UN)
Unnamed wife of Enosh – mother of Kenan (UN)
Unnamed wife of Jared – mother of Enoch & Shep (FC)
Zillah – second wife of Lamech (the line of Cain), mother of Tubal-cain (UN)

PLEASE HELP ME BY LEAVING A REVIEW!

i would be very grateful if you would leave a review of this book. Your feedback will be helpful to me in my future writing endeavors and will also assist others as they consider picking up a copy of the book.

To leave a review:

Go to: amazon.com/dp/1956866302

Or scan this QR code using your camera on your smartphone:

Thanks for your help!

~

THE COMPLETE SERIES OF "THE CALLED"

Stories of these ordinary men and women called by God to be used in extraordinary ways.

A Carpenter Called Joseph (Book 1)

A Prophet Called Isaiah (Book 2)

A Teacher Called Nicodemus (Book 3)

A Judge Called Deborah (Book 4)

A Merchant Called Lydia (Book 5)

A Friend Called Enoch (Book 6)

A Fisherman Called Simon (Book 7)

A Heroine Called Rahab (Book 8)

A Witness Called Mary (Book 9)

A Cupbearer Called Nehemiah (Book 10)

The first six books of the series are now available in these two single volume sets:

The Called Series Collection Volume 1 (NT Books 1, 3, 5)

The Called Series Collection Volume 2 (OT Books 2, 4, 6)

Available in paperback, large print, audio, and for Kindle on Amazon.

Go to: amazon.com/dp/B09F6SM149

Or scan this QR code using your camera on your smartphone to see the entire series.

"THE PARABLES" SERIES

***An Elusive Pursuit* (Book 1)**

Twenty-three year old R. Eugene Fearsithe boarded a train on the first day of April 1912 in pursuit of his elusive dream. Little did he know where the journey would take him, or what . . . and who . . . he would discover along the way.

***A Belated Discovery* (Book 2)**

(*releasing Spring 2024*)

Nineteen year old Robert E. Fearsithe, Jr. enlisted in the army on the fifteenth day of December 1941 to fight for his family, his friends, and his neighbors. Along the way, he discovered just who his neighbor truly was.

ALSO BY KENNETH A. WINTER

THROUGH THE EYES

(a series of biblical fiction novels)

Through the Eyes of a Shepherd

Through the Eyes of a Spy

Through the Eyes of a Prisoner

THE EYEWITNESSES

(a series of biblical fiction short story collections)

For Christmas/Advent

Little Did We Know – the advent of Jesus — for adults

Not Too Little To Know – the advent – ages 8 thru adult

For Easter/Lent

The One Who Stood Before Us – the ministry and passion of Jesus — for adults

The Little Ones Who Came – the ministry and passion – ages 8 thru adult

LESSONS LEARNED IN THE WILDERNESS SERIES

(a non-fiction series of biblical devotional studies)

The Journey Begins (Exodus) – Book 1

The Wandering Years (Numbers and Deuteronomy) – Book 2

Possessing The Promise (Joshua and Judges) – Book 3

Walking With The Master (The Gospels leading up to Palm Sunday) – Book 4

Taking Up The Cross (The Gospels – the passion through ascension) – Book 5

Until He Returns (The Book of Acts) – Book 6

ALSO AVAILABLE AS AUDIOBOOKS

THE CALLED

(the complete series)

A Carpenter Called Joseph

A Prophet Called Isaiah

A Teacher Called Nicodemus

A Judge Called Deborah

A Merchant Called Lydia

A Friend Called Enoch

A Fisherman Called Simon

A Heroine Called Rahab

A Witness Called Mary

A Cupbearer Called Nehemiah

~

Through the Eyes of a Shepherd

~

Little Did We Know

Not Too Little to Know

~

ACKNOWLEDGMENTS

I do not cease to give thanks for you ....
Ephesians 1:16 (ESV)

... my partner in all things, LaVonne,
for choosing to trust God as we follow Him in this faith adventure together;

... my family,
for your love, support and encouragement;

... Sheryl,
for always helping me tell the story in a better way;

... Scott,
for the way you use your creative abilities to bring glory to God;

... a great group of friends who have read advance copies of these books,
for all of your help, feedback and encouragement;

... and most importantly,
the One who is truly the Author and Finisher of it all
– **our Lord and Savior Jesus Christ**!

FROM THE AUTHOR

A word of explanation for those of you who are new to my writing.

You will notice that whenever i use the pronoun "I" referring to myself, i have chosen to use a lowercase "i." This only applies to me personally (in the Preface). i do not impose my personal conviction on any of the characters in this book. It is not a typographical error. i know this is contrary to proper English grammar and accepted editorial style guides. i drive editors (and "spell check") crazy by doing this. But years ago, the Lord convicted me – personally – that in all things i must decrease and He must increase.

And as a way of continuing personal reminder, from that day forward, i have chosen to use a lowercase "i" whenever referring to myself. Because of the same conviction, i use a capital letter for any pronoun referring to God throughout the entire book. The style guide for most of the Bible translations do not share that conviction. However, you will see that i have intentionally made that slight revision and capitalized any pronoun referring to God in my quotations of Scripture. If i have violated any style guides as a result, please accept my apology, but i must honor this conviction.

Lastly, regarding this matter – this is a personal conviction – and i share it only so you will understand why i have chosen to deviate from normal editorial practice. i am in no way suggesting or endeavoring to have anyone else subscribe to my conviction. Thanks for your understanding.

~

ABOUT THE AUTHOR

Ken Winter is a follower of Jesus, an extremely blessed husband, and a proud father and grandfather – all by the grace of God. His journey with Jesus has led him to serve on the pastoral staffs of two local churches – one in West Palm Beach, Florida and the other in Richmond, Virginia – and as the vice president of mobilization of the IMB, an international missions organization.

Today, Ken continues in that journey as a full-time author, teacher and speaker. You can read his weekly blog posts at kenwinter.blog and listen to his weekly podcast at kenwinter.org/podcast.

And we proclaim Him, admonishing every man and teaching every man with all wisdom, that we may present every man complete in Christ. And for this purpose also I labor, striving according to His power, which mightily works within me.
(Colossians 1:28-29 NASB)

PLEASE JOIN MY READERS' GROUP

Please join my Readers' Group in order to receive updates and information about future releases, etc.

Also, i will send you a free copy of ***The Journey Begins*** e-book — the first book in the ***Lessons Learned In The Wilderness*** series. It is yours to keep or share with a friend or family member that you think might benefit from it.

It's completely free to sign up. i value your privacy and will not spam you. Also, you can unsubscribe at any time.

Go to kenwinter.org to subscribe.

Or scan this QR code using your camera on your smartphone:

~

Printed in Great Britain
by Amazon